THE STILL
by Keith Simpson

DEEPINGS HERITAGE

"Then took Mary a pound of spikenard, very costly,
and anointed the feet of Jesus,
and wiped his feet with her hair:
the house was filled with the odour of the ointment"
(The Gospel According to St. Luke)

(In the Bible lavender was known as 'spikenard')

THE STILL
by Keith Simpson
first published in 2008 by Deepings Heritage

ISBN 978-0-9555532-1-9

THE STILL

A Story of the Market Deeping Essential Oil Distillery.

This book is dedicated to
Aubrey Ball (1909 – 1996)

ACKNOWLEDGEMENTS:

I would like to thank the following people for making this book possible.

The late Mr Aubrey Ball who spent many hours showing me over the distillery building. Also his daughter Pat who later allowed me access to make detailed drawings.

Norfolk Lavender for allowing the use of certain of their publicity photographs and the photograph I took of the still and condenser on display in their restaurant.

Matt Simpson for designing the cover of the book

Susyn Andrews (Horticultural Taxonomist) for her information about lavender and details about Messrs J. & G. Miller of Mitcham.

The Science & Society Picture Library for the use of the pictures of the 1862 exhibition.

Mrs Mary Vinton for the information she supplied about her father (Richard F. Stroud).

Mr Arthur Day for allowing me to quote from his sister Florence's book 'History of the Deepings' and providing some of the photographs included in this book.

Mrs Doris Bellairs for allowing me to reproduce the two items from the Newborough distillery.

Mrs Ann Taylor for proof reading the text of this book.

Ordnance Survey for allowing reproduction of the early 20th century map of Market Deeping. © Crown copyright

Stamford Museum for providing access to the information about Bryan Browning.

Mr Paul Beard for the use of his article about the Holbeach distillery.

Preface

It is said that in Market Deeping in Lincolnshire in 1826 there were 1016 inhabitants. If you had visited this village on the southern border of Lincolnshire during that time you would have seen a fairly typical village; this one held a weekly woad market. Here there resided William Holland who was a local surgeon. Shortly after 1826 the good doctor and a partner founded an industry that produced essential oils and herbal medicines of such high quality that they would later win prizes in international exhibitions. The essential oil distillery and medicinal manufacture was in production under the founder and later his son from 1840 until 1899, after which another firm took over until approximately 1910. It was then acquired by a man who decided to grow and process chicory. He was, unfortunately, later declared bankrupt. However, even then, the story of this remarkable business was not over.

Before you read this book I feel it is helpful to know the definition of an essential oil. There are two groups of so-called vegetable oils occurring in plants. The 'fixed' or 'fatty oils' and the 'volatile' or 'essential oils', although the sharp distinction between these two 'oils' was not fully recognised until the 16th century. An essential oil is said to be any concentrated, hydrophobic liquid containing volatile aroma compounds from plants which are called aromatic herbs or aromatic plants. Essential oils have also, in the past, been known as ethereal oils, or simply as the 'oil of the plant' from which they have been extracted, for example 'oil of cloves'. The term essential does not mean that the oil is an especially important or fundamental substance within the plant. In this context, the term essential indicates that the oil carries the distinctive scent (essence) of the plant. Essential oils, as a group, do not need to have any specific chemical properties in common, beyond conveying characteristic fragrances.

Introduction

The first pharmacopoeia, which listed 600 drugs, is attributed to the Greek, Dioscorides (AD65). Later one of the most important books, on the use of herbs to treat illness, came from a surgeon in Emperor Nero's army. This latter work, with illustrations of the plants giving details of their uses, was highly regarded for fifteen centuries. Although many people believe that another Greek, Hippocrates (460 – 370 BC), should be credited with the introduction of the treatment of disease; new evidence (2008) suggests that the birth of medicine was even earlier and should be attributed to the ancient Egyptians who treated wounds with honey, resins and metals (certain metals have been shown to have antimicrobial properties). The Egyptians also used herbs such as castor oil, cumin, coriander and colocynth and chemicals such as calcium carbonate and magnesium carbonate in the treatment of disease.

The monks of Europe had their herb gardens and continued to use herbal remedies. Beautiful illuminated manuscripts concerning herbs are still in existence. The Church developed the first hospitals in England and, in their gardens, herbs were grown to be used to treat the sick. From these early beginnings until quite recently herbs have been used exclusively to treat illness. Medieval monks kept herb gardens; there was one in the gardens of Peterborough cathedral. When the monasteries were dissolved during the 16th century, people would still raise herbs at home. England's most famous work on the subject was Gerard's 'Herbal' which was published in 1597. It is true that, even in 2008, some herbal remedies can be purchased 'over the counter' in specialist shops, but modern medical practitioners rarely use herbal medicines for treating their patients.

There are other reminders of the age of homely medicine. Springs whose waters were thought to have 'magical' properties were special places for early man. The spring at Bath in Summerset was a special place for the

Ancient Britains. It was dedicated to Sulis who was the local goddess of the thermal springs that still feed the baths in the Roman ruins in that city. Sulis was the deification of spring-water, especially of thermal spring-water, conceived as a nourishing, life-giving Mother goddess. The Romans, after they conquered Britain, also regarded that particular spring as a holy place. They dedicated it to their goddess Minerva and, as was their way, they did not remove the ancient name but dedicated their temple to Sulis & Minerva. Later springs such as these were said to have healing properties and were referred to as 'spas'. Some were even referred to as 'holy' wells. There is a 'holy well' at Buxton; there was one at Braceborough, not too far from Market Deeping, This 'holy well' achieved the title of 'Spa' because of the apparent healing properties of the waters there. It was quite famous in the past and George III was treated there. There was a 'holy well' at Longthorpe in Peterborough. Some of the herbal medicine side of our forebear's lives can be pieced together by looking around our countryside. A visitor looking at the many varieties of wild flowers might not realise that some of these plants were used to treat illness. Today most people have forgotten how useful many plants are, although they may still use a few of them as herbs in their cooking. Some of the plants that were used to treat illness in the past can be found growing in gardens today but now they may well be pulled up and burnt as weeds!

The experts in the use of herbal medicine were called apothecaries but whereas physicians and surgeons were officially recognized in the 16th century the apothecaries were not officially recognised until 1617. The sick not only went to the apothecaries for medicines, they also visited them for medical advice which upset the physicians and surgeons. This exacerbated the rivalry that already existed between these latter two professions as there was now another 'medical' man vying for the attention of the sick. This rivalry continued for many years and in 1618 the physicians published the first 'pharmacopoeia', a list of materials for making medicines. In 1649 the apothecary Nicholas Culpeper annoyed the physicians by translating their 'pharmacopoeia' from Latin into English. The original pharmacopoeia continued to be published for two hundred years. In 1858 the General Medical Council was created by Parliament and one of its duties was to compile and keep up-to-date the work, now called the British Pharmacopoeia (B.P.). The initials B.P. can still be seen today

(2008) on prescriptions and on the labels of modern medicines.

It is not surprising that doctors in the 19th century followed the old tradition and used herbal extracts for medicines, ointments, lotions and liniments even though the actual active substance within the 'herb' may not have been known. Two hundred years ago a certain Dr. Witherington of Birmingham examined a brew of herbs with which Mother Hutton of Shropshire had been using to successfully treat dropsy. He found she was using the leaves of foxgloves, the most common variety of which is *Digitalis purpurea* (the purple flowered variety). He experimented with a powder made from the leaves of this plant and thus discovered digitalis, later to be synthesised as 'digoxin'. Digoxin is important in modern times for the treatment of heart disease. Many of the substances extracted from plants in the 19th century are, in the 21st century, synthesised by the large pharmaceutical companies. However, even today there are drugs that cannot be synthesised and therefore still have to be extracted from plants. Vincristin, a drug used to treat certain cancers, is one of those drugs that cannot be synthesised. It is extracted from the leaves of the Rosy Periwinkle *(Catharanthus roseus).* Anna Lewington in her book 'Plants for People' states that to produce 100 grams of Vincristin requires 53 tons of Rosy Periwinkle leaves. As you can see the actual amount of active substance, when extracted from any particular plant may be very small.

In the early part of the 19th century, when William Holland and William Page established the 'Market Deeping Essential Oil Distillery and Medicinal Manufacture' they too had to produce their medicines from plants. The distillery ceased production in the early 20th century although the distillery building was not demolished until 2006. There are still a few reminders of the old ways. Some people still cultivate herbs, old preparations might still to be seen on chemists' shelves; there are herbalists' shops and it is said that there are even hospitals that still use herbal remedies. At Market Deeping William Holland's house in Church Street can still be seen though it is now used as a residential home for the elderly.

The following interesting extract comes from the autobiography of Jane Eyles who was born in 1887. "One day I was sent to the Chemist's shop in Market Deeping to buy something; I forget what it was. On entering the

Market Deeping

Godsey Lane/Tinkler Street

Distillery Buildings

Church Street

River Welland

shop I saw the Chemist Mr. Linnell, an old gentleman (he and his son ran the business). He was busy; so I waited and just watched what he was doing. He had a square frame with wires like harp strings stretched down and across with a board underneath on which were placed worm like lengths of something. A lever at the side cut the wormlike substance into small squares. I watched him finish this; then he looked up and said "What do you think I am doing, little girl?" I said "Making pills, sir" So he asked, "How do you know that?" I said, "Because my Mother makes some pills with dough and turpentine and rolls them in sugar. They are for my Grandfather because he has a bad back"

The manufacturing of drugs on a large scale dates from the mid to late 19th century, as the chemists moved from plants and minerals to synthetic drugs. However, for many years until quite recently, there were still to be seen in chemist shops many types of syrup, powders and other preparations bearing the names of the doctors and others who made them.

Some of the preparations are still familiar as are some herbs, for example senna pods. Not everyone believes in the healing properties of plant extracts. Even in the 21st century there is often heated debate about the benefits of herbal medicines. Some people advocate their use where others call it all 'quackery'. We must not forget that there are still medicines that can only be obtained from plants. It is thought that there may be many plants, as yet undiscovered, in the rain forests of our world that might contain substances that can be used in man's fight against disease. In the past willow bark was used to treat headaches, today Vincristin is extracted from rosy periwinkle leaves to treat cancer. Who knows what discoveries might yet be made from plants for the benefit of mankind?

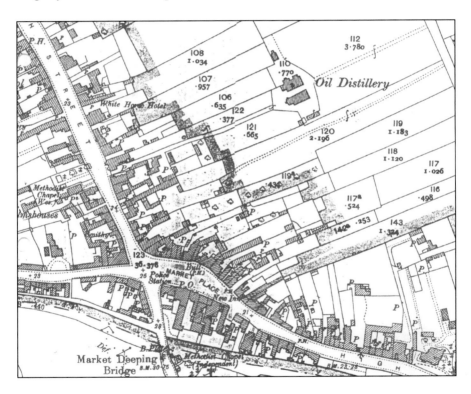

CHAPTER ONE

The History of the Market Deeping Distillery.

When setting out to write this chapter of the book I felt that I should try, if I could, to clear up the various idiosyncrasies in the historical narrative relating to this distillery. To do so I have read a great deal about the production and use of the various essential oils and herbal medicines. I have used what information was available locally and analysed it in the light of knowledge gained by talking to people who are experts in the field of lavender and/or peppermint essential oil production. I have also made an extensive study of the Market Deeping distillery building itself.

The production of essential oils and medicines in Market Deeping began in the early part of the 19th century when William Holland and William Page, two local surgeons, decided to go into production for themselves instead of buying the various products from other sources. Most stories I have heard suggest that they did this because they were dissatisfied with the quality of the products then available. Below I have quoted verbatim from Florence Day's book 'History of the Deepings' in which she suggests that the distillery was set up by one man:-

> Thus it happened when Mr. Holland who had come as a medical practitioner in Market Deeping, being dissatisfied with the quality of drugs and extracts supplied, conceived the idea of growing herbs and manufacturing his own medicines. He started in a small way with only one copper in the open and later in a little shed with a thatched roof where the distillery now stands (*The book was published in the 1970s when the distillery building was still standing*). Before long the good Doctor advertised for a qualified man, well versed in the growth of medicinal plants together with an all round knowledge of agriculture and horticulture. In answer to this advertisement

came Mr. Barker from the north in a coach - perhaps the Hull-Lincoln and London Mail. He had to tell Mr. Holland that if the 'Still Field' was all the land available, he had better take the coach back home at once. However Mr. Holland was pleased with the interview and promised to acquire more land as soon as possible. The field known as the Rector's field was the first to be rented from the Rev. R. W. Hildyard and about 1829 Mr. Barker came to live in Market Deeping.

When, many years ago, I first read the above story I thought it strange that any medical person would attempt to produce drugs and herbal extracts of better quality than those available at the time by 'boiling the appropriate plants in a copper in the open'. In fact, for many years I thought that the story of boiling the herbs in a copper in the open was just too quaint to be true and was more likely to be part of local folk lore. I then came across information that steam distillation of peppermint was 'invented' in America in 1846. The information regarding this invention stated that 'prior to 1846 the peppermint plants were boiled up in a copper and the essential oil was skimmed off when it rose to the top'. If this information is true (and I have no reason to doubt it) then the story of boiling plants in a copper in the open does not seem so strange after all. Although the article referred specifically to peppermint I have assumed that the technique applied to the extraction of essential oils from any plants.

Florence Day's story continues:-

As Mr. Holland bought and rented more land the business rapidly increased and at the time of Mr. Barker's death in 1876 the estate consisted of 1200 acres of both arable and pasture land. Being acknowledged as one of the finest cultivated spots in the county, we are told that farmers came from long distances to see and learn something of hedging and dyking. Four hundred of the twelve hundred acres were used for the cultivation of various herbs which included Aconite, Hemlock, Rosemary, Belladonna, Dill, Rue, Caraway, Henbane, Thornapple, Camomile, Lavender, Thyme (lemon scented), Cucumber, Peppermint, Clover, Poppy (white), and even Twitch! The fields of lavender in bloom are said to have equalled the tulip fields for beauty.

Elderly people still recall going for walks along the lanes then bordered with high hedges now alas with building estates - and enjoying the sweet scent of growing herbs. Many men, women and children were employed - the women going to work in their long dresses with print aprons and bonnets. Boys from the ancient school had three weeks' holiday round about Whitsun every year to enable them to earn money by helping to plant mint. It seems the grown ups made the holes and the children put in the plants. In due course Mr. Holland's son entered the business and the older man built a sort of watchtower by the side of the Tinker's Lane so that he could sit in it and enjoy watching his workpeople among the herbs.

Dandelion roots were brought in during the winter months by some of the cottagers and bought by Mr. Holland for so much a cwt. The roots of the liquorice plant were imported. The essential oils and extracts were in great demand and were sent to many parts of the United Kingdom and also abroad. Numerous medals were gained at various exhibitions including London, Paris and Berlin. Products of the distillery were purchased by the Apothecaries hall in London and were especially asked for on account of their excellent quality. Peppermint water was given away at the stile to parishioners and others who came long distances to fetch it. I remember an Aunt saying that she always took a bottle back with her to Leeds when she returned home having been to James' Deeping Feast. It was taken hot for colds and stomach ailments.

William Holland (surgeon and distiller) died on the 15th May 1851 and the younger William Holland sometimes referred to as Billy and sometimes as 'Squire', took over the running of the distillery. It is the younger William Holland, who is thought to have been the person who expanded the business. Confusion will always arise if the two people (father and son) being discussed both have the same forename. The younger William died in 1899 and, because there were no children to inherit the business, his widow put it up for auction. The auction was announced in the press as:

IMPORTANT ESTATE SALE IN SOUTH LINCOLNSHIRE.

THE LATE MR. W. HOLLAND ESTATES UNDER THE HAMMER

On Thursday last Mr J. G. Metcalf offered the estates of the late Mr. W.

MARKET DEEPING

TO BE SOLD BY AUCTION, BY

Mr. J. G. MEDCALF

On MONDAY, OCTOBER 2nd, 1899,

By order of the Executors of the late Wm. Holland, Esq.

Upon the DISTILLERY PREMISES, CHURCH STREET, MARKET DEEPING.

Office Furniture

SEEDS,

WAGONETTE, PONY HARNESS

WOOD, BUILDING MATERIALS,

OLD COPPER, IRON, AND EFFECTS

Viz.:—Office table, 4ft. 6in. by 2ft. 6in., high desk, large double pedestal writing desk, 4ft. 6in. by 3ft. 6in., deal table with 2 drawers, cupboard, chest of small drawers with papers bolt cupboard over, 2 chairs, 2 price charts, leather cisterns, bench and trough, quantity of boxes, 2 casks of mill lime, barrel screener, iron bins and copper scale and service, 200 dozen wine bottles, 500 dozen Winchester quart bottles, stone barrels, quantity of agricultural seeds, wheat chaff cutter by Ransell, large quantity of driving harness and reins, double set of pony harness, saddle harness, small waggonette, nearly 17 dog kennel, set of steps, 2 pony ladders, hand and wheel cart barrows, hand water cart, new dray rake, quantity of garden and other herbs, small iron roll, 10 wood baskets, potato riddles, potato measures, large quantity of flower pots of various sizes, large grindstone and frame, corn sieves, 2 wicker screens, corn bags weighing machine and weights, scales and weights, 2 hand trucks, several cwts. of old iron and copper, grand winding drum, well seasoned oak less about 500, 20 bars of fencing and firewood, quantity of billets, some wrought, 2 wheelbarrows 200 sanitary drain pipes, quantity of building coping, chandlers and fire bricks, garden frocks, 400 blue and red 6 in. floor tiles, about 2 tons of coal, and miscellaneous effects.

Sale to commence at Twelve o'clock at noon.

Auction Office, Market Deeping, Sept. 12th, 1899.

Holland J.P., for sale by auction at the White Horse Inn, Market Deeping. There was a large company present, and the biddings throughout were very spirited. 24 lots out of the 25 offered were disposed of under hammer and it was understood that the lot withdrawn was immediately afterwards disposed of at the reserve price. At the commencement the auctioneers pointed out that although South Lincolnshire was looked upon as a purely agricultural district, the property he had to offer had a considerably greater value attached to it than an agricultural one, as it included a valuable essential oil distillery and medical extract manufactory which was undoubtedly the most valuable property in Market Deeping that had been brought under the hammer during the present age as no expense had been spared to bring the concern to its present perfect state. He pointed to the very large profits that were constantly being made by all kinds of manufacturers and mentioned that some of the largest and best country seats were at the present time occupied by gentlemen who had made their 'pile' at that business. The sale included the goodwill and effects used in the working of the concern. "The business" he stated, "was originally started on a very small scale, between 60 and 70 years since. The late Mr Holland's father was a medical practitioner in Market Deeping and even at that date, he had the present day evils to contend with especially adulteration. He, therefore, conceived the idea of manufacturing his own medicine and commenced to distil the same by erecting a copper in the open. The experiment answered, and was continued for some time in a shed. The late Mr Holland was then a very young man and seeing the result of his father's experiment and, no doubt bearing in mind the words of Shakespeare 'There is a tide in affairs of men which, when taken in the flood, leads on to fortune,' he seized his opportunity, with the result that the above words had been fully justified". The Auctioneer also stated that the vendors knew it would be necessary to have about 300 acres of land to carry on the business successfully, so they had decided to offer lots 1 to 11 as a whole in the first instance, and if not sold, then separately.

The first eleven lots, consisting of an 'excellent residence in Market Deeping, the oil distillery and the medicinal extract manufactory with many items relating to the distillery business. These items include: 5 copper stills, 5 pewter condensers, an 8 horse power steam engine and a force pump together with a never ending supply of water. The Hall Farm with the Old Wakes Manor House, another farmhouse and altogether 300 acres of land (part copy hold) were then offered. The bidding commenced at £10,000 and at £15,100 the property was knocked down to Dr. Baker, 56, Finsbury Circus, London. *The steam engine and the force pump are thought to have been used to pump water. I was told by Mr. Aubrey Ball (senior) when he showed me around, that there was a large reservoir of water under the eastern end of the distillery building itself. The Deepings had no mains water supply in until the 20th century so an underground water supply was vital for the business. To carry out steam extraction requires many hundreds of gallons of water each day. Water would have been pumped from the source under the still itself, and possibly others that may have existed nearby, to the water tanks in the upper floor and on the roof. The water could then have been fed by gravity to the various stills and condensers as needed during the distilling process.*

To enable the reader to interpret the rest of the sale I have included definitions of the various terms used to measure areas of land. The letter 'a' means acres (an acre is equivalent to 0.40468 hectares. A hectare is equivalent to 10,000 square metres). The letter 'r' means roods (a rood = 0.25 acre) and I believe the letter' p' means either poles or perches. Apparently poles and perches and even rods appear to be the same thing (a pole or perch is equal to 30.5 square yards which is equivalent to 25.292 square metres).

The next lot, consisting of 7a. 5r. 4p. of arable land in Market Deeping Common, was sold to Mr. Thomas Davies, of Billingborough, for £320. A similar lot of 7a. 0r. 34p in the Little Common, was sold to Mr. Wade, solicitor, of Market Deeping, for £320.

The next piece consisted 21a. 3r. 34p., of arable land also in the Common, and this was passed at £600, later on it was put up and again withdrawn at £650, Mr. V. Stapleton being the last bidder; immediately after the sale however, it was disposed of at the reserve figure of £700. Dr. Benson, J.P. of Market Deeping, purchased a parcel of copyhold pasture land, at Deeping St. James and Mr. Wade of Market Deeping, was the purchaser of 3a. 2r. 8p. of copyhold arable land, in Langtoft, for £140.

A house in Langtoft with farm buildings an 83a. 0r. 9p. of land was knocked down to Mr. Watts of Toft (formally of Deeping St. Nicolas) for £2,800. Mr. A. Kingston of Buckton, Hunts, was the purchaser of 2r, 27p of copyhold land in Langtoft, for £35; and Mr. Wm. Gray, of Baston Fen bought the next, lot, 19a. 3r.18p.of arable land in Langtoft and Baston for £675.

The property next submitted was a walled in garden and ornamental ground, in Church Street Market Deeping covering half an acre and this, after spirited competition, was knocked down to Mr. G. G. Vergette for £190. A house, with harness maker's shop and paddock, in Church Street Market Deeping, occupied by Mr. Henry Strickson was sold to the tenant for £295. A house in Church Street, Market Deeping in the occupation of Mr. F. Swift was purchased by Dr Baker for £215. The next lot, including a house in Church Street, Market Deeping with garden and orchard covering 5 acres, was knocked down to Mr. Hildyard, solicitor, of Stamford for £630 and the same gentleman secured the next lot, two newly erected cottages, for £260. Mr. Maples, solicitor, of Spalding, bought the last lot of the sale cottages in Market Deeping for £610. Messrs. Phillips, Evans & Co., of Stamford, were the solicitors for the vendor and the sale altogether was considered a good one.

After the distillery was sold at auction in 1899 to Dr. Baker it appears to have passed through other hands until it was taken over by Richardsons, a firm from Leicester. Later it was reported to be owned by Mr August Paven who attempted to grow and process chicory. When Richardsons owned the business they employed a man called Richard F. Stroud. He worked (possibly as the manager) at Market Deeping from 1899 until he went to live in America in 1909. In the early part of the 20th century he wrote to a local newspaper and mentioned that he had in his possession some plans for the Market Deeping distillery. These plans were dated 1834 (for a laboratory) and 1836 (for an essential oil distillery). Florence Day says that Mr. Barker came to Market Deeping to work for William Holland in about 1829. The dates on the plans suggest that work to expand the business started soon after.

With plans being drawn up in 1834 and 1836 it seems likely that the distillery, or 'Still' as it became known locally, was built in the early 1840s. Accepting that steam distillation was not introduced until after 1846, it is possible that they continued producing the herbal medicines using the technique of boiling the plants in a 'copper' and skimming the oil off as it rose to the surface. After William Holland, son of the founder took over after his father died (after the advent of steam distillation in 1846) I assume he would have replaced the simple coppers with the type of boilers used for steam extraction.

When I visited the distillery building in the 1990s I found four intact furnaces and the remains of a fifth. Because the boilers used in conjunction with those furnaces were made of copper and had brass lids, they had been sold for scrap many years previously. I know, from visiting the lavender farm at Heacham in Norfolk and looking at pictures of the distillery process in distilleries in France and others in this country, that the extraction of essential oils from the various herbs after 1846 was undertaken using steam. Because I have not seen the original plans, or those of any subsequent alterations to the distillery building, I have no means of knowing how the extraction of the essential oils was carried out immediately after the distillery was constructed. I assume that steam extraction would have been introduced as soon as possible after its invention as that method would produced essential oils of much higher quality than the 'boil it up – skim it off' method.

Although there were no boilers in situ when I visited Market Deeping distillery there was other evidence indicating that steam distillation equipment had been present such as the winches used to lift the heavy lids off the boilers. The sale document in 1899 mentions 5 copper stills, 5 pewter condensers, an 8 horse power steam engine and a force pump.
In the notes of Richard F. Stroud, copies of which were sent to me by his daughter, he mentions purchasing 5 pewter worm condensers (there had been 5 copper stills). During the steam distillation process worm condensers, enclosed in a cold water tank, would have been used to condense the steam and oil vapour back to a liquid state so that the two could then be separated.

It is true that the essential oil production in Market Deeping was initiated by William Holland and William Page *(Pigot's directory of 1835 lists Holland and Page Surgeons & distillers of essential oils, Church Street, Market Deeping). (Pigot's Directory of 1841 lists Holland and Page - Surgeons and distillers of essential oils. Church Street)*. William Page is said to have left the business a short time later. *(White's directory of 1842 lists (i) William Holland, surgeon and distiller of essential oils and extracts (ii) Surgeons Holland and Page. All at*

Market Deeping). Although, of course, this does not exclude William Page from being connected with the distillery. I discovered information in Lincoln archives that suggests that William Page was still involved many years later. In the box of material on the Holland family there is listed an agreement as follows: - *10/10/1862 - Agreement for granting lease of land in Market Deeping in the county of Lincoln. William Page (distiller) agrees to lease all that piece of arable land in Hall Meadow, Deeping St. James to William Holland (12 acres 18 poles).*

In Kelly's directory of 1913 Mr. August Paven is listed as the manager of Hollands Distillery (essential oils) limited. He is also listed as a dairyman of Church Street, Market Deeping. Although Mr. Paven was still described as a distiller when he was declared bankrupt in 1921, the name of the Holland essential oils distillery appears to have been sold to a firm in Mitcham in Surrey in 1913.

However, the story of the essential oil industry in Market Deeping should not only be about William Holland, William Page, Richardsons of Leicester and anyone else who actually owned the business. To produce the various essential oils and medicines, for which this factory was famous, required more than one or two people! It obviously needed experts skilled in the production procedures. It also required men, women and children to carry out other tasks involved in the planting, growing, hoeing, cropping, carting, loading and unloading of the stills and stoking the fires that heated the stills. Particular attention needed to be paid to hoeing because, before the advent of chemical weed killers, hoeing the fields where the various herbal plants were growing would have been the method used to remove any weeds. This required many people spending a large amount of time in the fields. The removal of those plants (weeds) that were not part of the actual crop under cultivation would be necessary because any plants, other than those needed for the particular essential oil, would have contaminated the final product. Remember, this distillery was world famous and won prizes in many international exhibitions. Any contamination of their products would have ruined their reputation. Even if chemicals had been available it unlikely that they would have been used as chemical residues might also have contaminated the final product.

During the weeks when peppermint was being processed, the distillery would be on the go round the clock with the stills being filled and emptied three times in a twenty-four hour period. Apparently, the actual steam distillation of the essential oil would take a relatively short time. The majority of the time would be taken up with loading the boilers with the plants, stoking the fires to heat up the water to produce the steam and then, after the process was completed, removal of the exhausted material and its disposal.

Peppermint and lavender oils were the two major substances produced at this world famous distillery. This resulted in the appearance of many of the fields in the surrounding area. Not many farmers had large fields of lavender and peppermint but in the region around Market Deeping such fields were a common sight!

The price of peppermint oil was quite high and very profitable. I have given the costs of the various peppermint oils in decimal currency for ease of understanding.

In 1860 English peppermint oil was sold for £1.25p per lb. (£2.75p Kilogram).
American oil would only be sold for 35p per lb. (77p per kilogram).
By 1880 English peppermint oil was being sold at £1.75p per lb (£3.85p per kilogram).
American peppermint oil had also increased in price to 60p per lb (£1.32p per kilogram).
Japanese peppermint oil was selling for 50p per lb (£1.10p per kilogram).
Strangely, by 1900, English peppermint oil was being sold for £2.25 per lb (£4.95p per kilogram). American had dropped to 30p per lb (66p per kilogram) and Japanese was selling at just below 20p per lb (44p per kilogram)

The actual cost of peppermint oil on the open market did not reflect quality. English peppermint was of very high quality, so much so that the peppermint oil produced at the Market Deeping distillery was mentioned in the Encyclopaedia Britannica as of fine quality. When it came to competing with the foreign producers of peppermint oil the English producers had one very big problem. The production of English peppermint oil was very labour intensive. This reliance on a high number of man hours to produce the oil was reflected in the high cost of English peppermint oil. American peppermint oil and possibly, Japanese peppermint oil, was produced using a more mechanised process. This mechanisation of harvesting and extracting the oil improved the efficiency of production and this was then reflected in the lower cost on the open market. Richard F. Stroud mentioned the mechanisation of the peppermint oil in America when he wrote to the local press in the early 1900s.

Originally English peppermint oil was said to be of the very best quality and therefore the higher price could be justified. American peppermint oil and that produced in Japan would have incurred higher transport costs which would have increased the actual cost to the users. However there were reports that, to increase their profit, some of the more unscrupulous English producers mixed the cheaper American oil with their own. This resulted in a lowering of quality of the 'English' oil which, of course, meant that American peppermint oil was able to compete more favourably with their English counterparts on the quality of their oil. There may well have been many other factors involved in the failure of the English peppermint industry. The high production costs together with the adulteration of English Peppermint oil with 'other', cheaper oil would certainly have contributed greatly to the demise of the peppermint production in this country. If the English producers had introduced mechanisation they may have been able to compete, but they didn't so they couldn't!

To give some idea of the actual labour involved in the production of essential oils at Market Deeping one has only to look at the distillery at Crowland/Newborough, run by Perkins Bellairs. Market Deeping essential oil distillery had approximately 400 acres of land under cultivation for herbs. Perkins Bellairs had only sixteen acres of peppermint under cultivation and for that he employed 10 men for a fortnight in the spring, 12 women all the summer to keep it free from weeds and six men for three weeks in the busy month of August to do distilling. I do not suggest that the Market Deeping distillery, with its 400 acres would have had to have employed 25 times as many people at the same sort of times as Mr Perkins with his 16 acres. Dorothea Price and Joy Baxter, in a book they wrote about the Holland family said that the distillery employed 60 men on a full time basis. The two William Hollands were farming 1200 acres in total (although only 400 acres were used for growing herbs). The number of people they employed could have been 60 or have exceeded that number; the information on this is very sketchy. However, if you look at the photograph (page 45) of the school children busy in the distillery fields you can gather some insight into the scale of part time employment of the Market Deeping distillery.

Market Deeping Essential Oil Distillery not only produced peppermint and lavender oils, it was also involved in the production of medicines extracted from plants. With the advent of 'modern' medicines the use of those produced by the processes used at Market Deeping would have declined. Not only did the production methods change, the actual medicines themselves changed. Substances such as Opium, Belladonna and Strychnine, for example, would have quickly disappeared from chemists' shelves. When the more efficient manufacture of medicines started in the latter part of the 19th century it became difficult to for distilleries to compete. A large part of the problem was the labour intensive methods used at by distilleries like the one at Market Deeping. One hundred years ago, when herbal medicine production at Market Deeping ceased, the world was shortly to know of antibiotics.

Even in the 21st century people are still using herbs. Apparently many of the drugs produced today are still extracted from plants. Some plants, such as herbs or spices, are used in cooking. Some are sold over the counter in specialist shops for their supposed curative properties. Herbs and herb extracts are used to treat various ailments even though there are vast numbers of the more, so called, conventional medicines available to treat those same ailments. In the 21st century people can decide for themselves whether they want to use 'conventional' or herbal medicines. In the 19th centuries and those centuries before, herbal medicines were the only ones available.

CHAPTER TWO

The Essential Oil Distillery Building.

The Holland Essential Oil Distillery and Medicinal Manufactory originally consisted of four buildings. The smallest housed the toilet facilities for the workers at the distillery; the second was part bonded warehouse, part offices with stables on the ground floor. The third was a fairly large building used for drying the herbs prior to processing. I was unable to examine this particular building because it had been demolished many years before my visit to make way for a housing development. According to Mr Ball this building was known locally as the 'Chicory House'; this name is thought to have come about when the person, who owned the distillery in the early part of the 20th century, attempted to grow chicory to be turned into an essence for the 'coffee' industry (older readers may remember 'Camp Coffee'). It is assumed that he used the building that other owners had used for drying herbs, to dry the chicory plants prior to processing. The fourth building was the actual distillery itself. Sometimes referred to as the 'Still', this is where the various processes occurred that turned plant material into world class essential oils and medicines.

It is a shame that there is little information in the public record about the way the Market Deeping essential oil business was conducted but, by studying the main distillery building in detail, I have been able to draw some conclusions as to the way the various processes took place. I am grateful to the late Aubrey Ball for taking the time to show me over the main distillery building as it enabled me to take many photographs and make detailed measurements of the building's external and internal dimensions.

Many years ago the roof of the main building was severely damaged during a particularly stormy night when one of the tall chimneys collapsed. It had crashed through the roof and taken out a lot of the floor below. This structural damage to the roof together with the effect over the years of further stormy weather had, despite Mr Ball's attempts to prevent it, allowed rain to penetrate into the floors below. Due to the effect of the rain the floors were in a very poor condition, some were more like parchment than wood! Mr Ball had laid out the boards over these more dangerous parts of the floors and placed ladders where stairways had been damaged. To follow Mr Ball, as he clambered over the ladders and boards he had put in place, was no easy task but the effort was well worth it.

I realise that it might be difficult to follow my descriptions of the layout of the different areas and rooms that I saw and have therefore included outline drawings that I made together with some photographs of specific areas. Even as I write this book I am trying to find copies of the plans of the distillery produced in the early 19th century. Richard F. Stroud, who was manager of the distillery from 1899 to 1909, wrote to the Spalding Free Press in January 1936 saying that he had in his possession plans that were drawn up for a proposed new laboratory for W. Holland Esq. of Market Deeping dated March 28th 1834. He also had the plans of a proposed new distillery for the same gentleman dated 24th March 1836. There is little doubt, wrote Mr. Stroud, that all the plans were drawn by the same architect as they are dated at Northorpe in the same handwriting but no signature appears on them.

Although the name of the architect did not appear on the plans I believe it to have been a man called Bryan Browning. To obtain information as to who would have been living in Northorpe during the time mentioned, I contacted someone I knew in the Bourne Family History Society (Northorpe being just a few miles south of Bourne). He looked though the various censuses for the village and could only find one architect listed in the 19th century; that architect was Bryan Browning. Northorpe, more a hamlet than a village, is situated a few miles north of Market Deeping. The Browning family had been well known in Northorpe for at least two centuries. Bryan (1773-1856) was an architect of some repute locally who practiced at 16 Broad Street, Stamford, in the late 1830s. He was the

Layout of Ground floor distillery building

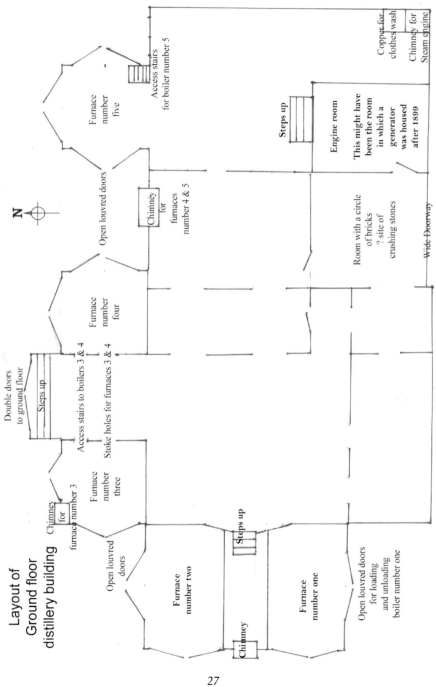

N

Chimney for furnace number 3

Furnace number three

Open louvred doors

Double doors to ground floor

Steps up

Access stairs to boilers 3 & 4

Stoke holes for furnaces 3 & 4

Furnace number four

Furnace number five

Access stairs for boiler number 5

Open louvred doors

Chimney for furnaces number 4 & 5

Steps up

Engine room

This might have been the room in which a generator was housed after 1899

Copper for clothes wash

Chimney for Steam engine

Room with a circle of bricks ? site of crushing stones

Wide Doorway

Furnace number two

Steps up

Chimney

Furnace number one

Open louvred doors for loading and unloading boiler number one

Layout of First floor distillery building

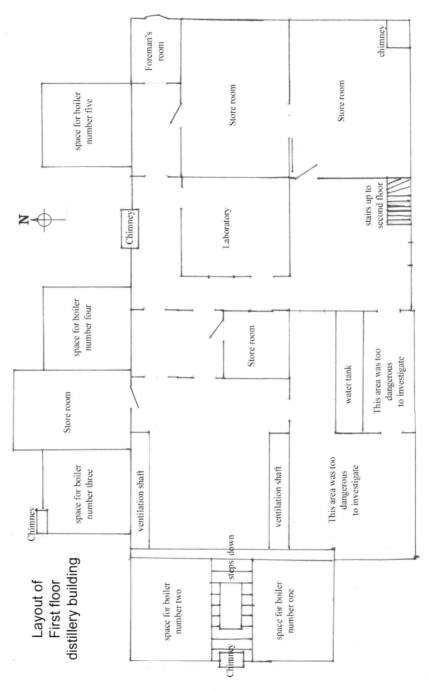

architect of Bourne Town Hall and Folkingham House of Correction. He was also responsible for considerable architectural work at Stamford, for example, the layout of Blackfriars Estate (1840), the YMCA buildings, the re-modelling of Barn Hill House (1843), work on St. Mary's Church, Grant's iron foundry, Byard House in St Paul's Street, etc. He was retained by the Marquis of Exeter as architect for the Burghley Estate in 1840 at a salary of £140 per annum. In Stamford museum there is an extensive list of the buildings that he designed, including the vicarage at Deeping St. James; However, Market Deeping distillery is not mentioned. If he had been the architect of the distillery one would have expected this impressive building to be on his list of achievements. The fact that it is not is puzzling but I still believe that Bryan Browning was the architect who drew up the plans mentioned by Richard F. Stroud. Bryan Browning's son Edward was also an architect and was responsible for designing the bridge at Stamford.

steam
engine
chimney

chimney
for still
number 3

North Side

Market Deeping essential oil distillery

By the time I visited the distillery the copper stills with their brass lids had long since been sold for scrap. Nothing remained of any of the other apparatus used to produce the vast number of essential oils and medicines that were made there. The plans of the main building and the laboratory (mentioned above) were brought back to this country by Richard Stroud's daughters and passed to a gentleman researching essential oil distilleries and perfumeries. The gentleman in question unfortunately passed away a short time later and his research material was placed in a London archive by one of his relatives. I have viewed the material, held in the 'Wellcome Museum for History in Medicine' in Euston Road, and have found some of it very useful to this project. However, the plans mentioned were not

Chimney connected to a Steam Engine

Eastern End

Market Deeping Essential Oil Distillery

Another view of the distillery building

Chimney connected to steam engine

Water tank

door into gound floor

Southern Side

Eastern End

included in the two large boxes of research notes and, not being able to see those original plans has hampered my research. I am not able to say if the building I viewed in the 1990s was the same as the original one constructed in the 1840s. As a result I cannot say with certainty whether there had been any major alterations during the lifetime of this distillery.

There were many places where doorways and windows had been blocked up. In one place on the ground floor there was a room that I believe had originally been an area outside the main building. The outside wall of this room protruded from the remainder by half a brick's width unlike the rest of the brickwork in the building. Inside, there were the remains of a metal stairway leading up to what looked like an external door on the first floor. All that remained of the stairway was part of the step supports and the metal handrail. The reason I feel that this area was originally outside the building is because this is the type of stairway one sees used as an external fire escape. This does not mean that this room was added after the original building was constructed but it is highly probable. Local sources suggest that when the younger William Holland took over from his father, in the

1850s, he greatly expanded the business. To have expanded the business may have required major alterations and, perhaps, the addition of more stills. To accommodate more stills may well have required major alterations to the building….. I do not know whether the five furnaces I saw when I visited were there originally. I believe I would have able to tell this had I seen the original plans. In the absence of the plans I have included the outline drawings I made of the ground and first floors where all the production took place. I have not included a drawing of the three store rooms on the second floor at the east end as no 'processes' took place there. The drawings, although in outline, are drawn to scale.

When I visited I found four intact furnaces and the remains of a fifth on the ground floor. The furnaces were arranged with three along the northern side and the other two at the west end. The main part of the furnace at the eastern end of the north side had been removed although I could see where it had been connected to the chimney. I was told that the furnace had been removed to allow space to park the family's car under cover. There was also the part of stairway leading to the first floor that was

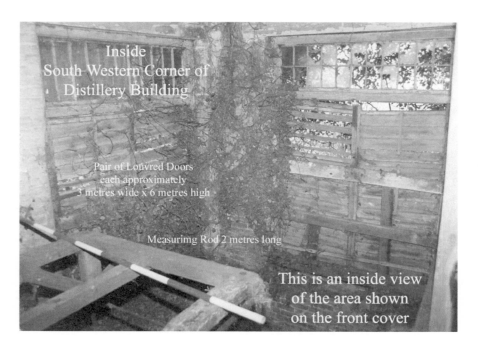

Inside
South Western Corner of
Distillery Building

Pair of Louvred Doors
each approximately
3 metres wide x 6 metres high

Measuring Rod 2 metres long

This is an inside view
of the area shown
on the front cover

The Distillery During Harvest Time

Offices and Bonded Warehouse

Water Tank

The men are standing in the south western corner of the building

associated with this missing furnace. On my initial visit I saw the laboratory in situ on the first floor but when I called on a later occasion the floor supporting it had given way and the remains of the laboratory were now in the ground floor area. Photographs I have included show some of the damage wreaked by the weather over the years.

Mr Ball showed me inside the garden store that had originally been an outside toilet for the workers. He also showed me the outside of the bonded warehouse that had been converted for use as a residence. I did not make a detailed study of inside of this building although I did look into the various store rooms (with outside access) on the ground floor that had originally been stables (there were even the remains of fittings on the walls that one might see in a tack room). Some of what I believe were the original windows on the first floor of the bonded warehouse/residence were still in place and had metal bars on them. These were there, one assumes, to prevent unauthorised removal of the 'bonded' goods originally stored inside.

The distillery building was constructed with its main axis running east to west. It was 82 feet (25.2 metres) long and 50 feet (15.4 metres) wide. The majority of the building was three storeys high although it was only two storeys high at the western end. The majority of the ground floor was

Some of the floors were more like parchment

actually about half a metre below the level of the outside ground with steps down. There were double doors on the north side of the ground floor that would have been used, I believe, for delivery of coal for the furnaces. Part of the ground floor (on the south side) was level with the outside ground. There were various rooms on this level; the largest one had a large circular arrangement of bricks built into the floor. This arrangement had, at its centre, a large groove, approximately 4 inches (about 10 cms) wide and 24 inches (60 cms) long. Mr Ball told me that there had been a mill stone in the garden when he first moved into the house many years previously. It might be that this arrangement of bricks with its central groove could have held the lower grind stone of a pair. The 1899 sale documents listed 'a pair of circular crushing stones working on a stone bed with iron frame'. This circular arrangement of bricks could well have been the site where these crushing stones were used. It must be remembered that William Holland was not only a distiller of essential oils; he also farmed more than 1500 acres of land. Only 400 acres of this was used for growing the herbs for the essential oil business, the rest was used for other crops and as grazing for animals. The crushing stones, mentioned by the auctioneer, might well have been used to produce animal feed.

The room immediately to the east of this arrangement of bricks was, according to Mr Ball, the 'engine room'. He said that although he had never seen an engine in situ he did remember that there had been a raised brick platform in the centre of the floor onto which an engine might have been seated. There was no engine present when I visited nor, according to Mr Ball, had there been in the previous 40 years. The platform to which Mr Ball referred was also missing. On the first floor I did find evidence of electrical wiring with switches sited near doorways at a height suggesting they were used to switch on a light to illuminate the room. Dorothea Price and Joy Baxter have written about the Holland family and, in their book which was published by Deepings Heritage, there is a list of items purchased by the Leicester firm of Richardsons after they had acquired the distillery in 1899. Under the heading 'Electric Plant' the list included a dynamo and an engine. I believe these were purchased by Richardsons to generate electricity. The electrical wiring I saw suggested that it was of a type used when the electricity was produced from a small generator. I do not believe there was electrical power in the distillery prior to 1899.

This electrical feature did not appear to have become permanent and was not present in the 1960s. In 1962 Mrs Mary Vinton and her sister visited the distillery and remarked, in a letter sent to me in 1999, that the house (previously the bonded warehouse) had no electricity and gas connected and that illumination was provided by paraffin lamps. Mary Vinton was one of the daughters of Richard F. Stroud who worked at the distillery from 1899 until he went to live in America in 1909. The daughters were visiting the area and wanted to see the place where their father had started his career in essential oil distillation.

As well as housing the five furnaces, the lower ground floor had areas where coal would have been stored (all the boilers were coal fired). Alongside each furnace, there was a narrow brick stairway leading to the upper level to enable access to the boiler associated with that particular furnace. The three furnaces on the north side were slightly smaller than the two at the west end. This suggested that they may not have been installed at the same time as the other two – perhaps another example of later alterations? Strangely, although there were five furnaces the building had only four chimneys. Stranger still, only three of the chimneys were connected to the five boilers. The two furnaces at the west end of the building were connected to one chimney situated midway between them. The two furnaces along the north side at the eastern end of the building had another chimney between them and the remaining furnace on the north side (at the west end) was served by a third chimney. On my first visit to the distillery the fourth chimney (at the western end of the south side) presented something of a dilemma as it did not appear to be connected to a furnace. There was no evidence of it ever having been connected to a furnace and strangely, it did not appear to be connected to anything else.

According to Mr Ball the three chimneys connected to the furnaces were originally all of the same height but the fourth chimney, mentioned above, had been much taller that the others. When I visited the distillery the chimneys that had been connected to the boilers were no longer at their original height. As I have already mentioned, one had collapsed during a particularly bad storm and after this storm Mr Ball had reduced the height of the other chimneys to prevent a similar occurrence. The tallest of the four chimneys was built into the corner of the building and would appear to be contemporary with it. Examination in the rooms on the two floors directly above the south east corner also suggested that this chimney was built at the same time as that part of the building.

I was puzzled by the fourth chimney because it did not appear to serve any useful function. Someone had, in the past, had a brick copper constructed adjacent to this chimney (perhaps to boil up the weekly wash). However, no fire used to heat a relatively small copper for the weekly wash would require a chimney of such height. This puzzle remained unsolved until I gave a talk about the Market Deeping distillery at a meeting on industrial archaeology. During the talk, I pointed out the puzzle of the tallest chimney. I also mentioned the possibility of an adjacent room being called the 'engine room' and that there were a lot of unexplained round holes about 15 cms in diameter in the walls of that part of the building. An engineer present asked if there had been a steam engine in the building but at that time I could not answer his question.

The engineer explained that, had there been a steam engine in use at the distillery in the early part of the nineteenth century, it would have required a very tall chimney to give sufficient draught. Furnaces, although

Remains of a windlass attached to still number one

requiring tall chimneys, did not require extremely tall chimneys of the type that early steam engines needed. He went on to explain that because early steam engines were not as efficient as the later models they required very tall chimneys to provide enough draught for the steam engine to perform efficiently (later models could perform effectively with a chimney of less height). I found out subsequently, after examining sale documents dated 1899, that there had been a steam engine in the distillery in the previous years which was used together with a force pump.

The extracting of essential oils from peppermint and lavender was, after 1846, by a process called steam distillation. This process used large quantities of water. There was no 'running' water in the Deepings during the 19th and early 20th centuries but, I have been informed, there were various underground sources of water close to the distillery. Mr Ball told me that there was a large reservoir of water under the eastern end of the distillery building itself. I believe that the water would have been pumped

Measuring Rod 2 metres long

Circle of Bricks
Possible site of
Crushing Stones

from below ground using a steam engine connected to a water (force) pump. The water was pumped up to be stored in tanks until required. When I visited there were the remains of very large water tanks on the roof and another situated within the roof space. When needed for the distilling process the water could have been fed by gravity to the appropriate boilers. The size of these tanks suggests that they would have been capable of holding extremely large quantities of water. Mr Ball said that the tanks on the roof had been used by local children in the past as a makeshift swimming pool.

On the first floor there were a number of storerooms and a small rectangular room that was said to have been used by the foreman of the distillery. At one end of this small room was a pair of windows set in a triangular frame. It is said that this allowed the foreman to keep an eye on the workers in the surrounding fields. The boilers were accessed from this floor. They were placed on a ledge about two feet below the floor level directly over each furnace. It was from this floor that the workers would have loaded and unloaded the boilers. When I visited there was a windlass adjacent to where one boiler had been sited and the fittings for other windlasses adjacent to where the other boilers had been. These windlasses would have been needed to provide the necessary leverage to raise and lower the heavy brass lids fitted to each boiler. There were the remains of pulleys attached to the rafters over each furnace. These would almost certainly have been used, together with the windlasses, to raise and lower the boiler lid.

This floor also had a large open space within which the workers would have performed the various tasks associated with separating the essential oil after processing and storing it until required. Towards the eastern end of the building, off a corridor close to the 'foreman's room' there was a room that was said, by Mr Ball, to be a laboratory. I could see no other purpose for it. The plans drawn up in 1834 mentioned a laboratory and this relatively small room appeared to have been constructed so as to be isolated from the rest of the building. There were two walls with lathe and

Remains of laboratory after it had fallen through to ground floor level

plaster and two walls constructed with the lower half of each made of wood and the upper half of glass panels. If delicate chemical processes were carried out in here I believe it would have needed to be isolated from the general dust etc. of the bulk processing part of the building.

The second storey (at the eastern end) would appear to have been used only for storage. There was a large wooden door on the south side of the main area. Attached to the roof directly above the door on the outside of the building was a pulley that would have been used to hoist various items up to this room. The door was sufficiently wide to accommodate large sacks of material. The wooden door itself was of interesting construction being very solid and having a large wooden bolt across the majority of its width. The main room ran the width of the building and there were two further rooms east of this. Both these rooms had had sliding doors mounted on grooves. The remains of the fittings were present although the doors had been removed. There was a similar fitted door on the first floor that showed the way such doors operated. The top of the door was suspended from an upper rail by a bracket with two small wheels attached. The bottom of the door was slotted into a metal groove fitted on the floor. The two small wheels allowed the door to slide easily and the groove at the bottom stopped the door swinging outwards.

The quality of workmanship in the construction of this building was remarkable. This was after all a factory in which a lot of dust and steam would have been generated. One does not, perhaps, expect the same quality of finish as would be seen in an office or a dwelling house. As well as in the laboratory, many of the other walls were covered with lathe and plaster. Where the plaster had been damaged the lathes could be clearly seen underneath. Even the underneath surface of the short flight of wooden stairs leading to the second floor was covered with lathe and plaster.

I have been informed by an engineer, who has seen the photographs of the distillery, that the brickwork was in the style of 'English Bonded', that is to say, constructed making the walls two bricks thick by placing two bricks one way and then the next two at right angles to them (there was no cavity wall). This type of construction apparently produces walls that are very strong. Using binoculars I examined the chimney at the south eastern corner of the building in relation to the wall against which it abutted. I could see no discernable difference in the gap at the top to that at the bottom. I carried out the examination in 1997 by which time the building had been standing for over one hundred and fifty years, with no major maintenance during the last 100 years. I wonder how many buildings constructed today will have their brickwork in such a good condition after one hundred and fifty years?

I was very impressed with this building and paid many visits over the years. After Mr Ball died his daughter, Pat, also allowed me access and I am grateful to her for this as it enabled me to take further measurements of the various rooms. The building was demolished in late 2006 to make way for a small housing development. Many local people objected to its demolition suggesting that it could have been used for some purpose or other. When I saw the distillery in the 1990s it was in such a poor state of repair that it would have cost more money than it was worth to bring it back to a state where it could have had a useful life. The distillery buildings were originally constructed in the middle of a field but, because of property developments over the years, they had become surrounded by large housing estates. If the main distillery building had later been developed for another purpose access to it, with the relatively narrow streets of these estates, would have been very restricted. It is sad that such a magnificent building has been demolished. I feel happy that, at least, it will not be forgotten.

CHAPTER THREE

The Distillation Process.

I mentioned, in chapter one that the initial production of essential oils at Market Deeping was by boiling the appropriate plants in a copper in the open. This is not the process I am going to describe here. It is likely, even if this was the method used in the early 1800s, that after the advent of steam distillation the 'boil it up – skim it off' method would have quickly become a thing of the past. The process used for extracting the essential oils out of the peppermint, lavender and other such plants was, after its introduction in 1846, that of steam distillation.

E. F. K. (Tim) Denny in his 270-page publication 'Field Distillation of Herbaceous Oils' (2001) was the first to show that the orthodox theory of essential oil distillation defied the second law of thermodynamics and discovered that transference of latent heat is the principle which governs the recovery of oils by steam distillation. According to Mr Denny the fundamental nature of steam distillation is that it enables a compound or mixture of compounds to be distilled (and subsequently recovered) at a temperature substantially below that of the boiling point(s) of the individual constituent(s). Essential oils contain substances with boiling points up to 200C or higher, including some that are solids at normal temperatures. In the presence of steam or boiling water, however, these substances are volatilized at a temperature close to 100C at atmospheric pressure. The mixture of hot vapours will, if allowed to pass through a cooling system, condense to form a liquid in which the oil and water comprise two distinct layers. Most (but not all) essential oils are lighter than water and form the top layer.

Tim Denny, who died in February 2008, forged an international reputation as the leading expert on lavender and the distillation of essential oils. He propagated new, more productive strains and developed improved

false bottom from one of the boilers

note the rows of small holes

husbandry techniques, designed and built the world's first lavender-harvesting machine and designed steam distillery equipment which improved both the quality and yield of lavender oil and the productivity of the stills.

When I saw the Market Deeping distillery building in the 1990s there were four large furnaces and, at the east end, the remains of a fifth. The two furnaces at the west end of the building were larger than the other three (I am assuming the two at the east end on the north side were of the same size). The copper boilers that would have been seated above these furnaces had a diameter of approximately 2 metres. The other three furnaces were slightly smaller and, one assumes, the copper boilers that sat upon them would also have been of a smaller diameter than those at the west end. The actual height of any of the boilers is unknown as they were sold many years before I undertook this study. I arrived at the approximate diameter of each boiler by measuring the gap across the upper ledge of the furnace on which the particular boiler would have been sited. In chapter eight there is a description of the distillery at Holbeach. One of the photographs in this book shows the inside of the barn at Holbeach where the stills were situated. You can obtain some idea of the actual size of those particular boilers by comparing them to the two men standing alongside. According to Mrs. C. M. Wilson in her article 'A Peppermint Distillery at Holbeach' in the Journal of Lincolnshire Industrial Archaeology. Volume 8 Number 1 (1973) each of the boilers at Holbeach were 10 ft. (3.1 metres) high and 6 ft (1.8 metres) in diameter. Although one may make assumptions about the height of the boilers at Market Deeping (knowing the approximate diameter) it does not follow that they would have had the same diameter to height ratio as those at Holbeach. I believe the only positive conclusion one can draw from knowing the approximate diameter of the boilers at Market Deeping distillery is that they were very big and held a large amount of plant material when loaded.

It is almost certain that the boilers were cylindrical in shape. From old photographs I have seen I believe that this was the shape of boilers used for peppermint and lavender distillation. I have also looked at photographs of the boilers in distilleries in Heacham in Norfolk, Holbeach in Lincolnshire and various places in Provence, France; all show this basic cylindrical shape. It would seem strange to change the shape that had been tried and tested over the years. Using a cylindrical shape would ensure that, once the lid had been raised, it would be easier for the exhausted plant material to be removed and the fresh material loaded. A cylindrical boiler could more easily be divided into two sections; a large upper section into which the plant material would be placed and a lower, smaller section which would hold the water that would be boiled to create the steam. I know the boilers at Market Deeping were made of copper as the 1899 sale documents stated this. I believe the boilers were made of copper because it is a metal that is easily worked, is a good conductor of heat and is the

Schoolchildren who are working in a field of peppermint

Looking down into one of the furnaces

Stoke Hole

The measuring rod is 2 metres long marked in 25 cm segments

least likely to corrode. All the pictures I have seen of modern boilers show that they are made of copper. If you visit 'Norfolk Lavender' you will see a copper boiler, with associated condenser, on display in the restaurant. Each boiler used for steam distillation would have contained a false bottom with numerous tiny holes completely separating the two sections. I discovered one of these 'false bottoms' behind the Market Deeping distillery building (see photograph). The holes in the false bottom allowed the steam to pass through into the upper chamber where it heated up the plants and extracted the oil as a vapour. The holes were large enough to allow the passage of steam but small enough to prevent plant material dropping through into the lower chamber. If plant material did get into the water it would have resulted in an oil of poorer quality.

On the top of each boiler would have been a heavy tight fitting brass lid with a spout through which the steam/oil vapour mixture would have passed into a condenser where the mixture would have been cooled back into water and oil, these two substances would then have passed into a container where they could be separated. The brass lid on the boilers would have been very heavy which meant that a windlass would have been needed to help raise and lower it at the appropriate time. The windlass would have been used in conjunction with a pulley system fixed to the rafter above each boiler. With the lid raised high above the boiler it would have been easier to pack the boiler with the appropriate plants and to remove the exhausted material at the end of the process. There was one windlass and the remains of fixtures for the others in the Market Deeping distillery.

The process of steam distillation was a simple one. The lower chamber would have been filled with water (thought to be approximately 400

Loading a still with lavender.
Note - stalks also included

Harvesting Peppermint by Hand

Note the sickle in boy's hand

gallons in the larger boilers) and the upper chamber would have been filled with the peppermint, lavender or other plant material. The lid was then lowered and tightened in place. The fire below the boiler was lit to heat the water below the plants. When the water began to boil, steam was generated. This steam passed up through the tiny holes in the false bottom, through the plants in the upper section, heating them up and extracting their essential oils. These oils, as vapour, together with the steam passed down the spout of the lid section and through a pewter condensing coil around which was a large volume of cold water. The steam/oil vapour condensed as it passed through the pewter coil and flowed, as a liquid, into a separator. The oil/water mixture separated and the essential oil was decanted off at various times during the course of each extraction.

When lavender was distilled the stalks would have been included with the flowers to ensure a fairly open texture to the material in the boiler. This would have ensured a good passage of steam through the lavender flowers. I understand that the essential oil of the lavender plant is contained in a gland just below the flower. It is thought that peppermint extraction would also have included bulk plant material for the same

Loading a still.

A Copper Still
and Condenser

NORFOLK
LAVENDER

reason. Peppermint and lavender oils were extracted in large quantities using the main boilers. Whether these boilers were used for the distillation of other essential oils I cannot say. It is possible that the processing of some of the medicinal plants may have been carried out in the laboratory. Production of some of the 'medicines' would have possibly been on a much smaller scale using smaller types of distillation apparatus, retorts, glass water condensers etc., similar to those that one might see in a school science laboratory.

Although the actual method by which the Market Deeping distillery produced the various medicinal extracts is unknown, it is fairly safe to assume that some of this was done in the laboratory area. Laudanum, an alcoholic extract of opium, was produced at Market Deeping distillery, together with many other narcotics, hence the need for a bonded warehouse (which was later used as a residence). When the peppermint and lavender plants were harvested from the fields they were allowed to dry out for 2 - 3 days before being processed. This measure ensured that

Drawing off the essential oil from above the water

any excess water in the plants would be removed and the ratio of oil to plant material would be increased (some estimates suggest that as much as 50% of the water could be removed this way). It is believed that the stills used in the distillery at Market Deeping would have yielded approximate 5 lbs (about 2.3 kilograms) of essential oil from each filling.

CHAPTER FOUR

The Products of the
Market Deeping Distillery.

In the early part of the 1800s there were no synthetic drugs of the types one sees on the pharmacy shelves in the 21ˢᵗ century. There were no antibiotics to help recover from infections. Pasteur had yet to describe his work on immunisation. If you became ill your doctor, without access to modern synthesised medicines, had to rely on those obtained from plants. The products of the Market Deeping distillery were so highly thought of that many their essential oils and medicines won prizes at the 1862 International Exhibition held in London.

Mary Vinton (daughter of Richard F. Stroud) sent me a little book with a list of the various chemists and other businesses that the distillery supplied. This list may, of course, also contain businesses that supplied the distillery with certain products that it needed. There is a reference to a firm in Marseille in France and, at least, 90 addresses in London alone. There are others in Birmingham; York; Liverpool; Lincoln; Manchester; Edinburgh; Boston; Glasgow and Brighton. Of particular significance was the name J. and G. Miller in Mitcham in Kent. This firm of distillers incorporated the 'Holland' name in 1913. That the Holland essential oil distillery of Market Deeping could have such a wide distribution of its customers speaks highly of the esteem in which it must have been held based, I assume, on the quality of its products.

To give a greater insight into the wide variety of essential oils and medicines that were produced in this distillery I have listed some of those prize winning medicines below. I have included details of their use in 19ᵗʰ century medicine and, in some of the cases, their use by herbalists in the 21ˢᵗ century. It must be stressed that the majority (if not all) of the products listed are poisons and would only have been used under the strictest supervision. Using plants to treat illness requires expert knowledge and should never be undertaken lightly. Hemlock, for example, was used to poison the Greek philosopher Socrates. Many substances and most medicines become poisons when taken in overdose. An overdose of aspirin can be fatal yet this product is widely available 'over the counter'. I want to stress that the products listed would only have been used in minute quantities and only then, under the expert advice and control of the doctor and/or an apothecary (pharmacist). It is extremely dangerous to use extracts of plants as medicines. No one would dream of collecting mushroom fungi from the fields without knowing whether they are edible or poisonous. It is the same with medicinal plants. The people producing and prescribing them were and are experts in their field.

The text explaining the use to which the various medicinal products were put may contain words that might be unfamiliar to the reader. I have therefore given a brief description of the meaning of some of them. This, I hope, will allow for a better understanding of the way the particular medicine was used.

Abortifacients – are substances that induce abortion.
Anodyne - a medicine that relieves pain
Antispasmodic - relaxes muscular spasms and cramps, calming nervous irritation.
Atonic Dyspepsia – is dyspepsia with impaired tone in the muscular walls of the stomach.
Biliary spasm – Abdominal pain in the region of the liver.
Cathartic – an agent for purging the bowels, especially a laxative.
Dysmenorrhoea - cramping abdominal pains experienced during, and sometimes just before, a woman's monthly period.
Demulcent - is an agent that forms a soothing film over a mucus membrane.
Dyspepsia - Chronic or recurrent pain or discomfort centred in the upper abdomen.
Dyspnoea - shortness of breath.
Electuary - is a medicinal paste composed of powders, or other ingredients, incorporated with some jam, honey, syrup, etc, for the purposes of oral consumption.

Emmenagogues - are herbs that stimulate blood flow in the pelvic area and uterus.

Fomentation - A quaint old term meaning the application of hot packs or a substance so applied.

Hydrosol - is the water (condensed steam) that is left over after the process of extracting an essential oil by steam distillation.

Incitant - Inciting; stimulating.

Inspissated - being thickened, dried, or made less fluid by evaporation

Oxytocic - Hastening or facilitating childbirth, especially by stimulating contractions of the uterus.

Peristalsis - is the rhythmic contraction of smooth muscles to propel contents through the digestive tract.

Rubefacient - is a substance for external application that produces redness of the skin.

Scrofula - is any of a variety of skin diseases; in particular, a form of tuberculosis.

Strobiles – are the cone like fruits of the hop.

Absinthii *(Wormwood)*

Wormwood consists of the fresh or dried upper leaves of 'Artermisia absinthium'

It was used to treat loss of appetite, dyspepsia, biliary spasm. Wormwood was one of the constituents of 'Absinthe' a controversial alcoholic drink that was thought to be responsible for the deterioration of the mental health of the painter Vincent Van Gogh.

Aconiti *(Extractum Aconiti Herbae)*

In the British pharmacopoeia Extractum Aconiti is listed as the inspissated juice of the fresh leaves and tops of the plant. It may be used in rheumatism, neuralgia, gout, scrofula, cutaneous diseases, inflammatory and febrile diseases, and in all cases in which the use of aconite is admissible. When the extract is of good quality it causes numbness and tingling in the mouth and lips shortly after taking it.

Aloes Socot. This preparation was indicated as a general tonic in cases of anaemia, anorexia, debility, headaches, low vitality, poor performance, poor liver function, indigestion, bloatedness.

Aloin (extracted from Aloe)

Is a naturally occurring, bitter tasting laxative property found in Aloe.

Aloes Barb. (another substance extracted from Aloe)

Was used as a purgative.

Anthemidis *(Camomile)*

Camomile was used as a mild tonic, in small doses acceptable and corroborant to the stomach, in large doses capable of acting as an emetic. In cold infusion it was often advantageously used in cases of enfeebled digestion in convalescence, of general debility, with languid appetite, which often attends convalescence from infectious fevers. The flowers were sometimes applied externally in the form of fomentation, in cases of irritation or inflammation of the abdominal viscera, and as a gentle incitant in flabby, ill-conditioned ulcers. The infusion is usually preferred. The decoction or extract cannot exert the full influence of the medicine, as the volatile oil is driven off.

Anethi Ang. (*Extracted from Anethum graveolens – Dill*)

Dill is an annual herb of the parsley family. It has a distinctive but mild caraway-like flavour. A winter crop, dill requires a well-drained, sandy soil with full exposure to sunlight. The sub tropical and temperate regions of India, particularly the northern parts, produce high quality dill. It was used as an aromatic carminative. The hydrosol has been known to be used for relieving flatulence in infants. Known as an expectorant with soothing effect it is said to lower the blood pressure in adults and is also effective for the treatment of colic, gas, and indigestion.

Gripe Water: - The first 'Gripe water' was formulated in England in 1851 and used by English nannies. The original Woodward's Gripe Water contained 3.6% alcohol, dill oil, sodium bicarbonate, sugar and water.

Anisi (*Extract of star anise*)

Attributed medicinal properties - Like anise, star anise has carminative, stomachic, stimulant and diuretic properties. In the East it is used to combat colic and rheumatism. It is a common flavouring for medicinal teas, cough mixtures and pastilles.

Belladonnae Viride *(Atropa Belladonna)*

Belladonna leaves are obtained from the deadly nightshade. The leaves and young branches are collected when the plant is in full flower and used while fresh or after drying. The chief constituents of belladonna leaves are the alkaloids atropine and hyoscyamine. The medicinal value of belladonna leaves is due to these two substances. The leaves were used principally in the form of the green extract, and in mixtures in the form of the juice. Occasionally the leaves were employed as an ingredient of cigarettes for spasmodic asthma. The medicinal property of belladonna root was used to check excessive secretion and to allay inflammation, particularly in secretory glands, such as the breast. Small doses were thought to allay cardiac palpitation. The plaster was applied to the cardiac region for the same purpose. It was found to be a powerful antispasmodic when used in intestinal colic and spasmodic asthma. It was given with purgatives when it depressed the inhibitory nerves of the intestine and allayed griping. Belladonna was said to be well borne by children and was given in large doses in whooping cough, urinary incontinence, and false croup. For its action on the circulation it was given in the collapse of pneumonia, typhoid fever, and other acute diseases. It was of value in acute sore throat, and relieved local inflammation and congestion. Belladonna decreases gastric secretion and was therefore not recommended to be taken just before or after meals. The root is the basis of the principal pharmaceutical preparations of belladonna (Belladonnae) and was suitable for mixing with olive oil or camphor liniment.

Colocynth. Co. *(Bitter Apple)*

Used as a purgative. In pre-modern medicine it was an ingredient in the electuary called 'confectio hamech' or 'diacatholicon' and most other laxative pills and in such cases as required purging, it was very successful. It is one of the most violent purgative drugs known insomuch that it excoriates the passages to such a degree as to sometimes draw blood, and induce a so-called 'super purgation'. Sometimes, in obstruction of the menses, it was taken boiled in water or beer which was considered successful in strong constitutions. Some women used it in the same manner, in the beginning of pregnancy, to cause an abortion, which often occurred due to the violence of its operation. Its usage for this purpose is documented in ancient times for example a recipe was found in a medical papyrus found in Egypt, dated to about 1550 B.C. The powder of colocynth was sometimes used externally, with aloes in unguents (ointments) and plasters with remarkable success against parasitic worms.

Cascarae Sagradae. *(Rhamnus purshiana)*
Is a mild cathartic laxative and was primarily used in the treatment of chronic constipation. Synonyms - Sacred Bark, California Buckthorn.

Conii – *(obtained from Conium Maculatum - Hemlock)*
Sometimes called 'poison parsley' it is an anodyne and narcotic. Succus Conii was used internally for its sedative and antispasmodic properties (see Coniina). Externally, as Unguentum Conii, it was a soothing application to haemorrhoids and other painful or irritable conditions of the rectum and anus.

Cannabis ind.
Medical marijuana was used, under medical supervision, for analgesia (pain relief). However marijuana was only used for analgesia in the context of a handful of illnesses, for example, headache, dysentery, menstrual cramps, and depression.

Carui. Ang. *(oil of caraway)*
Oil of caraway was used to impart flavour to medicines, and to correct their nauseating and griping effects. It was, at one time, recommended to be used in the treatment of scabies. Employing a solution in castor oil containing five parts of alcohol and oil of caraway in seventy-five parts of castor oil.

Cinnamomi *(cinnamon)*
Was prescribed for impotence, frigidity, feeling of cold and pain in the loins and knees; dyspnoea in deficiency of the kidney; dizziness, inflammation of the eye and sore throat due to yang deficiency; precordial and abdominal pain with cold sensation, vomiting and diarrhoea in deficiency-cold syndrome; neurosis with a feeling of gas rushing up through the chest to the throat from the lower abdomen; amenorrhea, dysmenorrhoeal. (*When one sees such a long list of conditions for which cinnamon is prescribed it might have been considered a 'wonder drug'!*)

Cymini *(cumin)*

Folklore superstition during the Middle Ages cited that cumin kept chickens and lovers from wandering. It was also believed that a happy life awaited the bride and groom who carried cumin seed throughout the wedding ceremony. Cumin was also said to help in the treatment of the common cold by adding it to a hot milk drink.

Copaiba *(Copaifera –a South American leguminous tree)*

As an anti inflammatory medicine copaiba has been used to treat stomach cancer and ulcers and has antifungal properties, among a very wide variety of other ascribed medicinal properties.

Caryoph- Ang. *(Oil of Cloves)*

Oil of cloves is obtained by distillation from the unexpanded flower heads of Eugenia caryophyllata (a rain forest flower). Oil of cloves, like other volatile oils, is antiseptic and antiputrescent; it is often employed as a preservative of organic substances when its odour is unobjectionable. Externally it was a rubefacient, a counter-irritant, and slightly anaesthetic; mixed with 2 parts of olive oil it could be applied to neuralgic areas and, as Linimentum Succini Compositum, it was employed as an embrocation in bronchitis, whooping cough, and rheumatism. Internally, oil of cloves was used as an antispasmodic and carminative.

Coriand. Ang. *(Coriander)*

Because of similar shape and usage, coriander leaves are named after parsley, often with a geographic epithet, for example, 'Indian parsley' or 'Chinese parsley'. Coriander eases the pain caused by spasms, stimulates the appetite and also disguises the unpleasant taste of other ingredients.

Cubebae *(Piper cubeba)*

Piper cubeba, or tailed pepper, is a plant in the 'genus Piper'. It is cultivated for its fruit and essential oil. The taste is pungent, acrid, slightly bitter and persistent. It has been described as tasting like allspice, or like a cross between allspice and black pepper.

It was used in the treatment of inflammation of the pharynx and larynx it was also used internally as an antiseptic diuretic, and as a stimulant to the genito-urinary mucous membrane, especially in the advanced stages of gonorrhoea. Cubebae was much used as a stimulating expectorant to the bronchial mucous membrane, and was the basis of some advertised bronchial lozenges.

Capsicin *(Obtained from Chilli Peppers)*

Capsicin was said to have been used as one of nature's best anaesthetics. Its action is to interfere with the action of substance 'P'. Substance 'P' is a nerve chemical that sends pain messages to the brain. Your body can only produce a limited amount of this chemical so when it runs out you become desensitised to the pain. Chillies are a great way to use up your substance 'P' and increase your body's collagenase and prostaglandin, thus reducing pain and inflammation. This is why chillies have been used as a folk medicine toothache remedy and as a pain reliever for cold sores, shingles, post surgical pain, puritis (chronic itching syndrome) diabetic neuropathy, frostbite, arthritis and a variety of skin problems. Chillies have been used in throat spray to kill pain and act as an antiseptic. *In November 2007 an article appeared in a national daily newspaper, outlining the properties of this substance. The way the article was written suggested that these properties had only recently been discovered. I understand from a local dentist that extract of chilli peppers might be used as a local anaesthetic in dentistry. It is often said that' what goes around comes around'.*

Colchicum *(Autumn Crocus)*

The corms of colchicum autumnale, the autumn crocus or meadow saffron, yield colchicine, which was once used to treat gout. Other members of this genus yield saffron which is used in cooking as a flavouring agent.

Digitalis *(Foxglove)*

Medicines from foxgloves are called 'Digitalin'. The use of *Digitalis purpurea* extract containing cardiac glycosides for the treatment of heart conditions was first described by William Withering, in 1785, which is considered the beginning of modern therapeutics. It is used to increase cardiac contractility and as an antiarrhythmic agent to control the heart rate, particularly in the irregular (and often fast) atrial fibrillation. It is therefore often prescribed, in modern medicine, for patients in atrial fibrillation, especially if they have been diagnosed with heart failure.

Ergotae Liq. *(from the fungus Claviceps purpurea)*

Historically controlled doses of ergot were used to induce abortions and to stop maternal bleeding after childbirth. Ergot is a fungus that has infected rye and other plants since farming began. One of the constituents of ergot, the ergot alkaloids, was found to have useful medicinal properties. Ergot was probably first used in medicine as an oxytocic drug. In 1582 Adam Loncier in Germany made the first note of ergot stimulating uterine contractions of labour. It was the most effective drug for this purpose at the time resulting in a rapid and sudden termination of labour, with a delivery time lasting less than three hours. But ergot was eventually deemed unsuitable for this purpose as the dosage could not be given accurately due to large variations in the active ingredients. Ergot also caused severe adverse effects, such as violent nausea and vomiting. In 1822 Hosack from New York stated that many stillbirths were due to uterine rupture resulting in maternal death. The use of ergot as an oxytocic was virtually abandoned by the end of the 19th century.

Elaterium *(Ecballium Elaterium)*

Was the name of a drug consisting of a sediment deposited by the juice of the fruit of Squirting Cucumber *(Ecballium Elaterium)* a native of the Mediterranean region. It was the most active hydragogue purgative known, causing also much depression and violent griping. The drug was undoubtedly valuable in cases of dropsy and Bright's disease, and also in cases of cerebral haemorrhage, threatened or present. It was recommended not to be used except in urgent cases, and would have had to be employed with the utmost care, especially 'if the state of the heart be unsatisfactory'.

Foeniculi Dulc *(Fennel seeds)*

Fennel contains anethole, an antispasmatic, alongside other pharmacologically active substances and this, or its polymers, act as phytoestrogens. This can explain some of fennel's action. Essential oil of sweet fennel was included in some pharmacopoeias. It was traditionally used in medicine to treat chills and stomach problems (carminative, antimicrobal action and so on). In fact, making a strong tea with fennel seeds was very effective in relieving bloating and gas. Fennel was also used as a digestive aid, especially in the lower intestinal area as it was said to relieve nausea and help the flow of digestive juices. Fennel leaves were often boiled, the steam given off was inhaled to relieve croup, asthma, and bronchitis. Fennel essential oil was used in soaps, and some perfumes.

Glycyrrh. (*Liquorice*)

The plant Glycyrrhiza glabra originated in the Mediterranean and the Middle East, but has been cultivated in Europe since at least the 16th century. It was commercially cultivated until recently in northern England. It was also an important tonic, often called 'the grandfather of herbs'. Glycyrrhiza was widely used in bronchial problems such as catarrh, bronchitis and coughs. It reduced irritation of the throat and yet had an expectorant action. It produced its demulcent and expectorant effects by stimulation of tracheal mucous secretion. Glycyrrhiza is also effective in helping to reduce fevers (glycyrretinic acid has an effect like aspirin), and it may have an antibacterial action as well. It was thought to be able to neutralise many toxins such as those of diphtheria and tetanus. Its anti-inflammatory action accounted for its use in the treatment of chronic inflammations such as arthritic and rheumatic diseases and chronic skin conditions.

Gentian (*Gentiana lutea*)

In medieval times, gentian was used in an alchemic brew 'theriac', a cure-all made to a highly secret recipe. Gentiana lutea was the most commonly used species in Europe. The part of the herb used was the root. It was traditionally used as a bitter digestive stimulant. The root was effective for conditions involving poor appetite or sluggish digestion. It was also used in fevers as it is cooling to the system. It is an antifungal agent, and was used to treat impetigo and for the treatment of serious heat burns and other injuries to the skin and gums.

Hyoscyami (*Henbane*)

Henbane was used for spasms of the urinary tract, stomach cramps, asthma, and tremors in the elderly. Hyoscyamus was used as a cerebral and spinal sedative, because of the hyoscyamine and hyoscine (scopolamine) which it contained. The comparatively small amount of atropine present did not give rise to the excitation and delirium occasioned by belladonna. It was therefore used in insomnia, especially when opium could not be given. Except for that difference it acted like atropine. Hyoscyamus was used to relieve the griping caused by drastic purgatives. Exactly how it acted was not known, but it appeared to act without diminishing the peristalsis; it was also a common ingredient of aperient (laxative) pills, especially those containing aloes and colocynth. It was given to allay irritability of the bladder and relieve pain in cystitis, and acted in precisely the same way as atropine. The tincture was given in mixtures as an antispasmodic in asthma in place of stramonium.

Juniperi Ang. (Juniper)
It was used to treat cystitis, in the absence of renal inflammation or other kidney disease, especially acute cystitis or urethritis. It was also used to treat chronic rheumatism. rheumatic joint and muscle pain, coughs, colds and catarrh, flagging appetite neuralgia, sciatica, diabetes, infected gums and bad breath. The herb was taken traditionally for fluid retention in children and so was deemed fairly safe if dosed appropriately. It was also used to treat intestinal gas and pain caused by wind. Juniper was used to help in menstrual pain, which was due to lack of tone of the uterine muscles. In olden days Juniper, also known by a folk-name of 'bastard killer', was taken over a number of days to try and effect a termination of an unwanted pregnancy. A high enough dose of most herbal abortifacients was likely to make you ill or vomit it all back up or suffer other side effects. Many women also died or suffered greatly from the dangerous bleeding, which could accompany a successful termination. Dried berries burned on charcoal and chipped wood make a good incense for a sickroom.

Jalapae (Ipomoea Jalapa)
The tuber of this plant is a resinous acrid herb with an unpleasant taste that was often used as a purgative. It was taken internally in the treatment of constipation, colic and intestinal parasites.

Krameria – (Obtained from a low shrub with large red flowers, growing on dry, sandy places on mountain-slopes, 3,000 to 8,000 feet above sea-level in several provinces of Peru)
A tincture of the root was found to be active as an astringent but could also act as a mild tonic. It was found to be useful for internal administration in chronic diarrhoea, dysentery, menorrhagia, incontinence of urine, haematuria, and passive haemorrhage from the bowels. It was also used as a gargle in relaxed sore throat and as an astringent wash for the mucous

membrane of the eyes, nose, gums, etc.

Lavand. Ang. *(lavender)*
The word Lavender is thought be derived from the French 'lavendières' or washerwomen who used it to scent their laundry. Lavender has been extensively used in herbalism for many years. English lavender, Lavandula angustifolia, yields a highly effective essential oil with very sweet overtones, and can be used in balms, salves, perfumes, cosmetics, and topical applications. French lavender, Lavandula x intermedia, yields a similar essential oil, with higher contents of turpin, which adds a harsher overtone to the fragrance. Essential oil of lavender has antiseptic and anti-inflammatory properties. An infusion of lavender is claimed to soothe and heal insect bites. Bunches of lavender are also said to ward off insects. If applied to the temples, lavender oil is said to soothe headaches. Lavender is frequently used as an aid to sleep and relaxation. Seeds and flowers of the plant are added to pillows, and an infusion of three flower heads added to a cup of boiling water is recommended as a soothing and relaxing bedtime drink. Lavender oil (or extract of Lavender) is claimed to heal acne when used diluted 1:10 with water, rosewater, or witch hazel; it was also used in the treatment of skin burns and inflammatory conditions.

Ginger *(Zingiber officinale)*
The term ginger is used to describe the edible part of the plant which is commonly used as a spice in cooking throughout the world. Often erroneously referred to as 'ginger root', the edible section is actually the horizontal subterranean stem or rhizome of the plant. The ginger plant has a long history of cultivation known to originate in China and then spread to India, Southeast Asia, West Africa, and the Caribbean. The medical form of ginger historically was called 'Jamaica ginger'; it was classified as a stimulant and carminative, and used frequently for dyspepsia and colic. It was also frequently employed to disguise the taste of medicines. Ginger is contraindicated in people suffering from gallstones as the herb promotes the release of bile from the gallbladder.

Humuli Lupuli *(also known as Hops)*
Hops are widely cultivated in Europe, parts of Asia, and North America. The female flower (or strobile) is yellowish-green. Hops taste bitter and the odour is characteristic and aromatic. They contain volatile oil,

flavonols, resin, and miscellaneous ingredients such as tannins and lipids. The strobiles were used as a sedative and to help combat sleeplessness when taken orally or placed in a pillow. Their bitterness when ingested made them an effective gastric stimulant, and they were found to help improve the symptoms of irritable bowel and incontinence. Hops were also used as a tonic, diuretic, and aromatic bitter and for their antimicrobial activity. Most commonly of course they are used in the production of beer.

Menth. Pip. Ang. *(Mentha Piperita. Peppermint)*

The genus Mentha comprises at least fifteen species, of which there are also a great many varieties. Some of the mints have been in use for culinary and medicinal purposes since antiquity, but no well defined distinction is made as to just what plants were employed. Mentha piperita L. is the most important member of this genus, and was, long ago cultivated by the Egyptians. It is mentioned in the Icelandic Pharmacopoeia of the thirteenth century. The oldest existing peppermint district in England is in Mitcham in Surrey. The medicinal properties depend on a volatile oil, of which from 1 to 1.25 % can be obtained from the herb. The leaves are said to contain a little tannic acid. The virtues of the herb are imparted to water, and more readily to alcohol. Peppermint is an aromatic stimulant, much used to allay nausea, relieve spasmodic pains of the stomach and bowels, expel flatus, or cover the taste of, or qualify the nauseating or griping effects of, other medicines.

Menth. Viride Ang. *(Spearmint)*

The carminative properties of spearmint are inferior to those of peppermint. Spearmint is chiefly employed as a diurectic.

Myristicae *(Oil of Nutmeg)*

Used to relieve Rheumatic pain. The oil of nutmeg unites to the common properties of the aromatics considerable narcotic power. A number of fatal cases of nutmeg poisoning have been reported in human beings. The toxic ingredient is myristicin. The oil of nutmeg is used to correct the taste of various drugs and as a local stimulant to the gastro-intestinal tract.

Nucis Vomicae (strychnine)

Small doses of strychnine were once used in medications as a stimulant, a laxative and as a treatment for other stomach ailments. Strychnine has stimulant effects at low doses but, because of its high toxicity and tendency to cause convulsions, the use of strychnine in medicine was eventually abandoned once safer alternatives became available.

Origani Ang. (*wild marjoram*)
Used as a liniment but also used to relieve toothache. Oil of origanum is a stimulant and rubefacient, but is chiefly employed in the form of liniment as an application to various parts suffering from painful affections. As with many other essential oils, it affords relief in toothache upon being applied to the decayed tooth by means of lint or cotton. It is very seldom administered internally.

Opii (*Papaveris - Poppy*)
The distillery produced opium and laudanum (an alcoholic tincture of opium). Opium is extracted from the opium poppy (Papaver somniferum) as are all the refined opiates such as morphine, thebaine, codeine, papaverine, and noscapine. Papaver somniferum loosely means the 'sleep-bringing poppy', referring to its narcotic properties. Opium poppies have a lilac coloured flower. Strangely, purple flowered poppies can be seen (in 2008) growing, almost as a weed, in many gardens in the Deepings. Whether the poppies grown by the Holland family, for processing in the distillery, were the ancestors of these plants is not known. Another poppy mentioned in the 1862 awards was Papaveris Alba (white poppy).

Pimentae (*Oil of Bay*)
Used to aid digestion.

Podophylli or Resina Podophylli
This is an active principle obtained from the root of the common May-apple (podophyllum peltatum). It is a powerful, though slowly acting, cathartic believed also to act more than most purgative medicines on the liver. It was usually administered with a laxative, for the removal of intestinal worms.

Pulegii
Oil of pulegium or pennyroyal is obtained by distillation from fresh pennyroyal herb. Oil of pennyroyal closely resembles, in its properties,

other volatile oils. It was administered on sugar, or with a draught of hot water, as an emmenagogue. During excretion it mildly irritates the kidneys and bladder, and reflexly excites uterine contractions.

Rosmarini Ang. *(Oil of Rosemary)*
This was used in perfumes and also in medicine for the treatment of colic and nervous disorders.

Rutae Ang. Oleum Rutae. (*Oil of Rue*)
An herbaceous plant indigenous to the Mediterranean countries – used to treat convulsions and hysteria. Oil of rue was used as a stimulant, antispasmodic, and emmenagogue. It had decidedly active properties. Locally it was an irritant, and internally, even in small doses, it produced severe gastro-intestinal and nervous disturbances. Oil of rue, in the dose of from 1 to 5 drops, 3 times a day, was used with advantage in hysteria, convulsions, pertussis (whooping cough), amenorrhea, and dysmenorrhoea. Although it was sometimes used for the purpose of producing a criminal (illegal) abortion, it was highly dangerous and caused many fatalities.

Sarzae *(made from roots of Jamaican sarsaparilla)*
Used (as Rad.Sarzae.Jam.) medicinally as a cure for gout.

Stramonii Fol.
The properties of stramonium are virtually those of the alkaloid hyoscyamine (found in henbane). The drug was used chiefly to relieve the spasmodic contractions of the bronchioles in asthma. The leaves were smoked in cigarettes, or are mixed with potassium nitrate and other anti-asthmatic substances, then burned and the fumes inhaled. The treatment was, however, only palliative and the causation of the attack was not affected.

Sabinae Ang. *(I have been unable to determine what this substance is. The name Sabinae is given, as part of the name, to a wide variety of plants a type of juniper tree and even a type of fish)* It was used to treat dysmenorrhoea and sterility and also said to cure genital warts.

Sinapis Essent. (*Dried seeds of Brassica hirta – Mustard*)
Mustard was used as an emetic and, of course, also used in the form of a mustard plaster.

Santal. Flav. Ang. (*Sandalwood*)
Used as a fragrance enhancer.

Succini (*Oil of amber*)
Used in amenorrhoea, hysteria, dysmenorrhoea, tetanus, epilepsy, pertussis (whooping cough) and infantile convulsions. Oil of amber was obtained from amber by destructive distillation, and purified by redistillation. Oil of amber has properties resembling those of oil of turpentine, and was sometimes given internally in the treatment of asthma and whooping cough. Mixed with an equal quantity of olive oil, or as Linimentum Succini Compositum (compound liniment of amber), it was used to rub the chest in bronchitis and whooping cough.

Sassafras
Sassafras is a genus of two species of deciduous trees in the family Lauraceae, native to eastern North America and eastern Asia. The essential oil distilled from the root-bark or the fruit was used as a fragrance in perfumes and soaps, food (sassafras tea) and for aromatherapy. The essential oil was also used as a pain killer as well as an antiseptic in dentistry. The smell of sassafras oil is said to make an excellent repellent for mosquitoes and other insects. A yellow dye is obtained from the wood. The leaves are used for thickening sauces and soups, and when dried and ground are known as filé powder, a spice used in Cajun, Creole, and other Louisiana cooking, such as the dish 'filé gumbo'.

Sassafras Pith (*Sassafras medulla*)
Was used as a demulcent, especially for inflammation of the eyes, and as a soothing drink in catarrhal affection.

Scammoniae
Scammony resin, a mixture of resins obtained from Scammony Root or from Orizaba Jalap Root, is a drastic purgative. Scammony resin was used as an energetic cathartic, likely to occasion griping, and sometimes operating with harshness. It was known to the ancient Greek physicians,

and was much employed by the Arabians, who used it as a purgative and externally in skin diseases. On account of its occasional violence, it was seldom administered, except in combination with other cathartics, the action of which it promoted, while its own harshness was mitigated. It was said to be given in emulsion with mucilage, sugar, almonds, liquorice, or other demulcent. Its disposition to gripe was said to be counteracted by the addition of an aromatic.

Scoparii *(Cytisus scoparius - Broom Tops)*
Scopari are the fresh and the dried tops of Cytisus scoparius. Scoparius is diuretic and cathartic, and in large doses emetic, and was employed with advantage in dropsy.

Taraxaci *(Taraxacum officinale) - Dandelion root*
Taraxaci was obtained from the common dandelion, Taraxacum officinale. Dandelion root was used as a bitter in atonic dyspepsia, and as a mild laxative in habitual constipation. It had no action on the liver. Dandelion was also said to be a rich source of vitamins and minerals. The leaves certainly have a very high content of vitamin A as well as moderate amounts of vitamin D, vitamin C, various B vitamins, iron, silicon, magnesium, zinc, and manganese. Even in the 21st century dandelion is commonly used as a food. The leaves are used in salads and teas, while in the past the roots were often used as a coffee substitute. Dandelion leaves and roots have been used for hundreds of years to treat liver, gallbladder, kidney, and joint problems. In some countries, dandelion is considered a blood purifier and is used for ailments such as eczema and cancer. Dandelion has also been used historically to treat poor digestion, water retention, and diseases of the liver, including hepatitis.

Valerian *(Valeriana)*
The root of Valeriana Officinalis has a strong smell, and is much used in medicine as an antispasmodic. It has been used as a medicinal herb since at least the time of ancient Greece and Rome. Hippocrates described its properties, and Galen later prescribed it as a remedy for insomnia.
Valerian was used in the past against sleeping disorders, restlessness and anxiety, and as a muscle relaxant.

CHAPTER FIVE

The 1862 International Exhibition.

At the international exhibition, held in London in 1862, Holland's distillery was given an 'Honoris Causa' (an honorary degree). The prize medals awarded were: - In class 2, for pharmaceutical extracts, essential oils and dried herbs of superior quality. In class 4, for essential oils of excellent quality. Below is a list of the pharmaceuticals and essential oils mentioned.

Oil of - Anethi Ang.; Anisi; Absinth. Ang.; Anthemidis Ang.; Aznygd. Essent; Carui.Ang.; Cinnamomi; Cymini; Copaiba; Caryoph. Ang.; Coriand. Ang.; Cubebae; Foeniculi Dulc.; Juniperi Ang.; Lavand. Ang.; Menth. Pip. Ang.; Menth. Viride Ang.; Myristicae; Origani Ang.; Pimentae; Pulegii Ang.; Rosmarini Ang.; Rutae Ang.; Sabinae Ang.; Sinapis Essent; Santal. Flav. Ang.; Succini; Sassafras.

Extract of - Aconiti (Viride); Aconiti (Alcohol. Rad.); Absinthii; Anthemidis; Aloes Socot; Aloes Barb.; Belladonnae (Viride); Cascarae Sagradae; Cascarae Sagradae Liq.; Conii; Colchici; Colchici Acet.; Cannabis ind.; Colocynth. Co.; Digitalis; Ergotae; Ergotae Liq.; Gentian; Glycyrrh.; Hyoscyami (Viride); Lupuli; Jalapae; Krameria; Malt; Nucis Vomicae; Opii; Rhei; Papaveris Alb.; Sarzae; Stramonii; Taraxaci; Valerian.; Lactucae.

Succus - Aconiti; Belladonna; Conii; Digitalis; Hyoscyami; Scoparii; Taraxaci;

Fol - Aconiti; Belladonnae; Conii; Digitalis; Hyoscyami;

Rad - Aconiti Ang; Belladonnae Ang.; Colchici Ang; Tarax. Ang.

Resin – Jalapae; Podophylli; Scammoniae; Gingerin; Capsicin; Aloin; Elaterium

The products of the Holland Essential Oil Distillery were said to be of very high quality and the awards they were given supports that. Market Deeping did not have 'running water' until well into the 20th century. Vast quantities of water were needed for the production of the essential oils and medicines and therefore the distillery had to rely on water obtained from underground sources. However, what might seem a difficulty may well have proved to be an asset. The water obtained from wells etc. may have contained fewer impurities than water obtained from a mains supply.

The International Exhibition of 1862, or Great London Exposition, was a 'world's fair'. It was held from May 1st to November 1st 1862 beside the gardens of the Royal Horticultural Society, South Kensington, London, on a site that now houses museums including the Science Museum.
The exposition was sponsored by the Royal Society of Arts, Manufactures and Trade, and featured over 28,000 exhibitors from 36 countries, representing a wide range of industry, technology, and the arts. All told, it attracted about 6.1 million visitors. Receipts of £459,632 were slightly above costs which were £458,842. This left a total profit of £790.
It was housed on 23 acres (9 hectares) of land, within a special building designed by Captain Francis Fowke (1823-1865) and built by Charles and Thomas Lucas and Sir John Kelk at a cost of £300,000. This cost was covered by profits from the Great Exhibition of 1851. The building consisted of a main structure with two adjoining wings set at right angles for machinery and agricultural equipment; the wings were demolished after the Exhibition. Its main facade along Cromwell Road was 1152 feet (351 m) in length, and ornamented by two crystal domes, each of which was 260 feet (79 m) high. Although they were then the two largest domes in the world, their effect was distinctly unimpressive, and they were derided as 'colossal soup bowls' and a national disgrace. The building as a whole was termed 'a wretched shed' by The Art Journal.

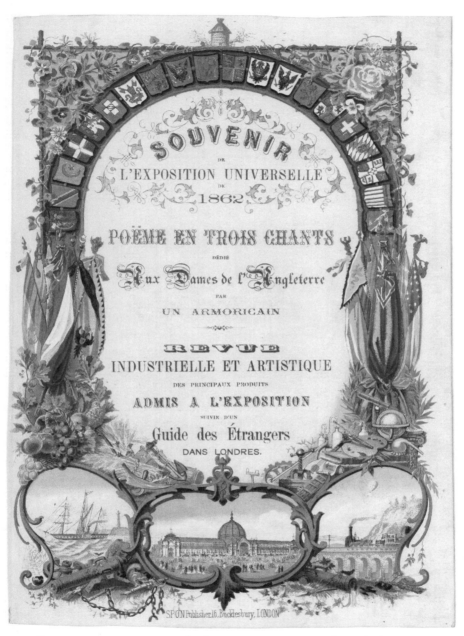

Souvenir poster of The International Exhibition

Building that housed the 1862 International Exhibition

Exhibitions included such large pieces of machinery as parts of Charles Babbage's analytical engine (said to be the first computer), cotton mills, and maritime engines by the firm of Henry Maudslay, as well as a range of smaller goods including fabrics, rugs, sculptures, furniture, plates, silver and glass wares, and wallpaper. The exposition also introduced the use of caoutchouc for rubber production and the Bessemer process for steel manufacture. Caoutchouc is an elastic material obtained from the latex sap of trees (especially trees of the genera Hevea and Ficus) that can be vulcanized and finished into a variety of products. When all was said and done, however, when compared to the Great Industrial Exhibition of 1851, the 1862 exhibition was generally judged a failure.

The judging panels (juries) were composed of 296 British and 271 foreign members spread over the 36 industrial and agricultural classes. There were 7,000 medals awarded and 5,300 honorable citations. The organizers of the 1851 Exhibition had given very careful consideration to the development of an Awards' System for that event which would recognize innovation of ideas and excellence of workmanship and production as separate and distinct criteria. They had also divided the exhibits into a readily comprehensible system of classification which ensured that broadly similar products would be competing side by side for recognition against each other rather than against the overall contents of the Exhibition as a whole.

Although the 1851 system was not perfect and was subject to abuse, it was a rational attempt to recognize various facets of excellence for the various categories of objects exhibited. There the Juries were very clearly instructed and appear to have applied very high standards to the granting of an award; only some 22% of the exhibitors in 1851 received any kind of medal, and most of those were clearly specified to be for workmanship rather than for innovation.

The Commissioners had most probably reverted to the single-medal approach to avoid the problems which had followed the 1851 awards of medal-winning exhibitors attributing their awards to criteria which were in fact irrelevant. A notable British example had been Richard Carte, who had claimed to have won a Prize Medal in 1851 for the design of his 1851 Patent flute, whereas in fact the award had specifically been won by

Rudall & Rose for their fine workmanship displayed in the manufacture of that instrument. By making all medals equal, the Commissioners doubtless hoped that such abuses would not be possible.

These problems and their inevitable attendant consequences were as obvious to contemporary observers as they are to us today, and the judging of the exhibits and awarding of medals and honorable citations attracted harsh criticism at the time. Some exhibitors even staged protests within the Exhibition building regarding their treatment at the hands of the Juries, and a great deal of bad feeling was engendered. In addition, the intrinsic value of the awards was substantially diluted - the very loose award criteria and the under-the-table deal-making which must have taken place among the Juries quite predictably resulted in no less than 12,300 of the exhibitors (42%) receiving awards (as opposed to only 22% in 1851). Consequently, the system could hardly be taken seriously as a true reflection of outstanding relative merit.

However, it was possible to identify certain trends from the statistics in connection with the awards process. When the dust settled, and despite having to compete on British soil under the terms laid down by a British organizing committee, France had still received 4% more awards than Great Britain, thus maintaining a slight but nonetheless appreciable edge in terms of recognition of her National accomplishments. This can hardly have sat well with the organizers or indeed with the British public! In addition, the medal itself, which showed Britannia, complete with her lion, laying her products at the feet of personifications of trade, industry and the arts, was denigrated as being 'too large and ugly'. The whole awards process left a bad taste in the mouths of many observers, both in Britain and elsewhere.

In summary, it must be said that in terms of the awards process and the true value attached to the granting of an award, the organizers of the 1862 Exhibition failed to build upon the work of their predecessors of 1851. As a result, the value and significance of the awards granted in 1862 were considerably diluted in comparison to those of the awards granted in 1851.

Even accepting the above comments, regarding the value of the awards granted in the 1862 Exhibition, the fact that the Market Deeping essential oil distillery and medicinal manufactory won awards for so many of its products shows that this distillery was of world class standard.

HOLLAND'S DISTILLERY,
MARKET DEEPING.

PRIZE MEDALS, 1862, AWARDED

IN CLASS 2 *for Pharmaceutical Extracts, Essential Oils, and Dried Herbs of Superior quality.*

IN CLASS 4 *for Essential Oils, excellence of quality.*

Ol. Anethi Ang.
,, —Anisi
,, Absinth. Ang.
,, Anthemidis Ang.
,, Amygd. Essent.
,, Carui. Ang.
,, Cinnamomi
,, Cymini
,, Copaibæ
,, Caryoph. Ang.
,, Coriand. Ang.
,, Cubebæ
,, Fœniculi Dulc.
,, Juniperi Ang.
,, Lavand. Ang.
,, Menth. Pip. Ang.
,, Menth. Viride Ang.
,, Myristicæ
,, Origani Ang.
,, Pimentæ
,, Pulegii Ang.
,, Rosmarini Ang.
,, Rutæ Ang.
,, Sabinæ Ang.
,, Sinapis Essent.
,, Santal. Flav. Ang.
,, Succini
,, Sassafras

Ext. Aconiti (Viride)
,, Aconiti (Alcohol. Rad.)
,, Absinthii

Ext. Anthemidis
,, Aloes Socot.
,, Aloes Barb.
,, Belladonnæ (Viride)
,, Cascaræ Sagradæ
,, Cascaræ Sagradæ Liq.
,, Conii
,, Colchici
,, Colchici Acet.
,, Cannabis Ind.
,, Colocynth. Co.
,, Digitalis
,, Ergotæ
,, Ergotæ Liq.
,, Gentian.
,, Glycyrrh.
,, Hyoscyami (Viride)
,, Lupuli
,, Jalapæ
,, Krameriæ
,, Malt
,, Nucis Vomicæ
,, Opii
,, Rhei
,, Papaveris Alb.
,, Sarzæ
,, Stramonii Foi.
,, Stramonii
,, Taraxaci
,, Valerian.
,, Lactucæ

Succus Aconiti
,, Belladonnæ
,, Conii
,, Digitalis
,, Hyoscyami
,, Scoparii
,, Taraxaci

Foi. Aconiti
,, Belladonnæ
,, Conii
,, Digitalis
,, Hyoscyami

Rad. Aconiti Ang.
,, Belladonnæ Ang.
,, Colchici Ang.
,, Tarax. Ang.

Gingerin
Capsicin
Aloin
Elaterium

Resin. Jalapæ
,, Podophylli
,, Scammoniæ

CHAPTER SIX

Reports and Newspapers.

The Market Deeping essential oil distillery was often mentioned in learned journals and official reports. Below are four of them.

T. Nelson 'Rural Rides' 1830 Tour, April, London. 'The whole area around here described enthusiastically by Wm. Cobbet as being "Rich Arable Land". Lincolnshire the Productive County'

Chemical News volume V May 3rd 1862 page 302 – William Holland's well known reputation as a grower of medicinal plants and distiller of essential oils.

Wilson Fox. 'Report on the County of Lincolnshire' Royal Commission on Agriculture HMSO London 1895 page 105. 'In the neighbourhood of St. James Deeping a large farmer grows a considerable acreage of peppermint'.

The Perfumery & Essential Oil Record - 1935 page 76 Official County write up. 'Holland Distillery established 1840'

There have, in the past, been a number of reports in newspapers, of the growing of plants, for the production of essential oils and medicines, in the Market Deeping distillery. I have included two but have added my own notes to, what I regard as, errors in the reports. The following extract about the cultivation of lavender appeared in the Peterborough Standard dated 16th July 1921.

Headline - A Three-century old Industry with Possibilities

History has it that lavender was introduced into England in the year 1568 and that for a long time thereafter the home crop supported the bulk of the lavender oil used in this country. In comparatively recent times, however, the industry of lavender growing was sorely hit by a disease of the plant, and this had the effect of very much reducing the area under the crop. An article referring to this was published in an October 1883 edition of the 'Peterborough Standard'. This article stated that at Market Deeping in Lincolnshire, where lavender was formerly grown, the business had been discontinued because of disease. This led to an increasing importation of lavender from France and other countries. However, the quality of the imported produce was not as good as that grown at home and commanded a lower price on our markets.

The plant flourishes best on a warm, well drained medium loam with a slope to the south or south-west. A loam that is too rich is detrimental to the oil yield; as excessive nourishment tends to increase the growth of the leaf. Protection against summer gales by a copse or wood on the south west is also of considerable value, as these gales may do great damage to the crop by causing the tall spikes to break away at their junction with the stem.

As to cultivation, the land should first be carefully cleaned of weeds in the autumn, should be burnt, and the ashes distributed over the ground, together with some ordinary wood ash if obtainable. The soil should then be prepared by 'trenching in' a quantity of straw and stable refuse, but not much rich dung, and should lie fallow until the following spring, when any weeds remaining should be dealt with as before and the whole ploughed over. Towards late spring the young plants should be dibbled in rows running from north to south, 4 feet apart and 6 feet between the rows. These wide spaces are not more than is necessary to allow the plant to full growth for flower bearing, room for cutting flowers and for keeping the ground clear of weeds.

The crop is propagated from cuttings broken off with a root or heel and planted in March, April or September. The cuttings should be of young growth, and should first of all be planted 3 or 4 inches apart in a shady spot and kept watered. In the following spring they can be transplanted to their proper positions in the field. Weeds should be continually suppressed, but the hoeing should not be more than one inch deep, as the roots of the plant spread near the surface of the ground. Young plants should as far as possible be kept from flowering during the first year, by clipping so that the strength of the plant is thrown into the lateral shoots, to make it bushy and compact. A full picking is usually obtained from the second to the fifth years, after which the old plants should be cleared off and burnt, and the ashes put upon the ground. The land should then be ploughed, manured, cross-ploughed, and left fallow until the following spring, when re-stocking can commence.

The harvest is more or less dependent upon the season, but as a rule it begins in the first week of August, though if the weather is wet it will be best to leave the cutting of the flowers until later. The best oil is obtained after a hot droughty season. The flowers should be fully open when cut, and if required for distillation should be spread out on the shelves or on the floor of dry sheds until partially dry. It is estimated that about 1,200 pounds (600 kilograms) of partially dried flowers, yielding 25 pounds (11.4 kilograms) of lavender oil, is obtained from an acre of good land under favourable conditions. Much, of course, depends on the energy and careful superintendence of the grower, and also in the care taken by the distiller in the process of distillation. Last year (1920) distillers paid £40 to £100 per ton of flowers, according to quality.

In the Peterborough Advertiser dated Tuesday 17th 1928 there was a report describing the production of essential oils at the distillery in Market Deeping, Lincolnshire. I have, where necessary, made comments regarding the accuracy, as I see it, of the statements made.

Headline - Making Poisons and Drugs from plants at Market Deeping.
Sub-headline (1) - Squire Holland and his Remarkable Distillery.
Sub-headline (2) - Fields of Peppermint and Poppies
Sub-headline (3) - Curious Incidents and Stories of a Strange Industry

The distillery at Market Deeping, famous in the middle of the last century for its perfumes and poisons, is almost unknown to the present generation. Liquorice, laudanum and lavender water have lost their hold on people's lives. The shelves of our surgeries are filled with synthetic substitutes for old-fashioned herbal remedies like peppermint, while our chemists' shops are filled with newer perfumes, so the kilns and coppers of Squire Holland of Market Deeping, became relics of the past. But fifty years ago they were flourishing, tended night and day by men who ate the Squire's salt beef and fat bacon between great chunks of home-made bread after a long night's stoking at the distillery. Those certainly were the days. Few masters now stand in their kitchens on Christmas Eve, giving 8lb of pork to every married man, five to each bachelor, and three to all lads. The Squire possessed nine cows, too, and never sold a drop of milk all the year round. And all the time the scent and drug making industry flourished at Market Deeping.

Same Cabby for Fifty Years

Dr Holland, who was a physician as well as a farmer, started distilling herbal juices in a small way in the early part of the last century. After his death, his only son, William, took over, and the Still grew in fame. Apparatus - then the latest and best on the market - was installed, and every Friday the Squire went to London with his samples. At King's Cross he always took a certain cab, and the same man drove him for fifty years. *(William Holland junior was apparently known as 'Squire' Holland although the reason is not clear. He was, in fact, a farmer, distiller of essential oils and local Justice of the Peace).* The farm increased from 30 acres to 1,800 acres and 2,000 sheep were clipped yearly.

Producing Powerful Peppermint

Peppermint was the best known product of the Still. The Encyclopedia Britannica mentioned Market Deeping as having been an important centre for its manufacture. The plant favours rich, wet soil and Squire Holland's well-tilled fields were scenes of intense activity in August, when the crop was being cut by the men, raked for carting by the women, and gleaned by the boys. Then for six weeks the still was on the go day and night. Stokers kept roaring fires under the four great coppers *(actually there were five stills)*, each holding 5 cwt. of peppermint plant, packed tight by the heavy tread of stout Lincolnshire soles and heels. After four hours, the vapour had stopped passing through the condenser. The fires died down, the false bottoms of the coppers were raised, and the mass of pulp remaining was carted away to be mixed with manure, while the distilled oil was carefully corked down.

Perhaps 160 cwt. of fresh flowering herb would be obtained from every acre and for every 5 lbs there would be distilled 1 oz. of essential oil. *(There* are 20 cwts. *{Hundredweights} in 1 ton. There are 2000 lbs. {pounds} in 1 ton. In 160 cwts. there are 8 tons which equates to 16000 lbs. From every acre this would result in 3200 ounces or 200 lbs of oil. There are 2.2 lbs in a kilogram therefore 1 acre of land would yield approximately 91 kilograms of peppermint oil)* This peppermint oil was extremely powerful and, far from producing a feeling of cold on the tongue, it would taste like the hottest poker that ever was. Some residents can well remember when a small bottle was dropped at Deeping St. James station and a powerful odour permeated the platform for months.

Fields of Lavender

Lavender water, considered good for disorders of the head and nerves, if you believed in it, was made in much the same way, the essential oil being dissolved with spirits of wine, essence of musk, rose, bergamot and ambergris before being complete. The lavender fields at Market Deeping were a rare sight and a delicious smell. Just before harvest time in August old and young would join in the picking the flowers, and for every acre anything from 12lb to 30lb *(5.5 to 13.5 kilograms)* of lavender oil would be obtained, according to the dryness or otherwise of the weather. *(The main source of oil from the lavender plant is contained in a small gland just below the flower. The stem of the plant together with the flower would have been collected. The stems would have been included with the flowers when they were loaded into the boiler as this would enable the texture of the plant material to be open enough to allow the steam, used for extracting the oil from the plants, to pass more freely. If the flowers alone had been loaded into the boiler they would have quickly matted together preventing steam from passing through).* The oil, which was distilled over the first hour-and-a-half, was the best and was generally collected separately. Later came the ranker vapour from the stems.

Laudanum

While peppermint and lavender were the chief products, Squire Holland supplied chemists and doctors all over the country with laudanum which he got from poppies and black lettuce. *(I can find no reference for the manufacture of laudanum that includes lettuce, of any colour).* The poppy fields were another glorious sight in the heyday of this fascinating industry- in fact the whole countryside must have been redolent and reflective of this remarkable industry. Laudanum is an alcoholic tincture of opium, and has long been a favorite narcotic drug. Paracelsus, a famous physician of the 16th century, first gave the word 'laudanum' to a preparation of his own, reputed to be made of gold pearls, but largely composed of opium. His full name was Phillippus Aureolous Theophrastus Paracelsus, and his family name Bombastus, which explains a good deal.

The Apothecaries' Revenge

He was an amazing figure, and, after wandering over Europe studying medicine from nature, not note books, he became town physician at Basel, where he gave lectures in the University, criticising the current quackeries and attacking the ignorant pomposity and greed of those who practiced them. It is said that apothecaries (whose drugs found no place in his pharmaceutical system) threw him down from a steep place, but others believe he died in a low tavern after a drinking bout lasting several days. But this has taken us a long way from Market Deeping.

Liquorice From Dandelion Roots

Liquorice, a succulent if sticky sweetmeat, with a middle-class reputation, was the only thing that Squire Holland made that could be eaten. Dandelion roots from Langtoft, Bourne, Crowland and Eye were brought by the cartload to be turned into liquorice. Children living in the neighbourhood spent many happy days digging and grubbing for dandelion roots. They would dip their fingers in, too, for surreptitious tastes of liquorice in the making. *(Dandelion roots were from the plant with the Latin name 'Taraxacum officinale' and would not have been converted into liquorice. Dandelion roots would have been collected to be used as a medicine or converted into a substitute for coffee. Liquorice was produced from 'Glycyrrhiza glabra', another plant entirely)*

Remarkable Adventure of Mr. Todd

One, James Todd, strolled in one day and, seeing nobody about, he dipped deep and often. Or he would have done but he found himself staggering about the stillroom, which seemed to be circling round him. They found him later lying in the corner, a boy was hastily dispatched to fetch a Doctor - with a stomach pump - for it was belladonna on the boil, not liquorice! Todd got better, and lived to a ripe old age, but he never took any more liquorice on the sly. On another occasion seventy pigs got into a field of poisonous herbs and well, you know what pigs are! They buried them all a few hours later in a heap as far away from the town as possible.

More Deadly Herbs

Belladonna (deadly nightshade) is a powerful alkaloid, which was used as a local anaesthetic. Hemlock, too, was distilled for its virulent juice, from which, it will be remembered, Socrates died. Henbane produced another poisonous alkaloid, which had a tranquilising effect on people suffering from severe nervous irritability, though of old it was said that it made those who chanced to eat it 'to bray like asses or neigh like horses'. The smoking of its seeds or capsules was a somewhat dangerous remedy used by country people for toothache. From elder flowers, Squire Holland made a kind of soap for shaving and softening water.

Mr. Tom Palmer's Memories

In the winter Mr. Holland would get the village Schoolmasters for miles around to send the poor into Market Deeping, where they were given meat and soup (boiled in the coppers which had made peppermint and lavender water - but it did not seem to matter when there was fifteen degrees of frost). *(I find it difficult to believe that the coppers used for the essential oils would have used to boil meat. The essential oils produced by the Holland distillery were of a very high quality and any contamination from the remains of meat would have ruined the business).* After Mr. Holland's death in 1899, Mr. Dick Stroud and his son ran the Distillery for a firm of Leicester chemists, and later Mr. Payne, a Belgium, ran it for a French Firm, we believe, until the 1914 - 1918 war. *(Kelly's directory of 1913 lists a Mr. August Paven as the manager of the distillery. Richard F. Stroud did indeed work at the distillery from 1899 until 1909, possibly as the manager. He was born in Leicester in 1882 and would have therefore been too young to have had a son who would have been old enough to work with him at the Market Deeping distillery).*

CHAPTER SEVEN

The American Connection.

After William Holland, son of the founder, died in 1899, the distillery business in Market Deeping was sold by auction to a certain Dr. Baker of 56, Finsbury Circus, London. Apart from Dr Baker's name being reported in the press, as having bought the distillery and other properties owned by William Holland, I can find no other information about this gentleman. The information I do have suggests that the distillery passed through a number of hands during 1899 until it was acquired by a firm based in Leicester called Richardsons.

Richardsons employed at the distillery a certain Richard F. Stroud. In the 1901 census, Richard F. Stroud is listed as age 19 years, lodging at a boarding house in Mill Lane and employed as manager of a distillery (for essential oils and pharmaceutical extracts). Richard was born in 1882 in Leicester, St. Peter's. He worked at the distillery until migrating to America in 1909. To be manager of the Market Deeping distillery at the age of 19 years and to have achieved all he did after he migrated to America suggests that Richard F. Stroud was a truly remarkable man. Through various intermediaries I was able to make contact with one of his daughters who provided me with information about her father's time at the Holland Distillery in Market Deeping. The notes and letters written below were sent to me in 1998 by Mrs. Mary Vinton, Richard F. Stroud's 82 year old daughter who also sent me some extracts from her diaries.

'Tuesday August 14th 1962 Market Deeping'

Indeed a day to remember! After enquiries we walked down a narrow shrub lined path to where dad had had the distillery. Mr W. J. Adams, 5 years ill in bed, and his wife made us most welcome. The distillery is a shambles but we roamed it with Mrs Adams – she offered to send us the blown panel in the door of the laboratory – signatures scratched in it date back to 1861. They asked us to stay the night but we could not. They have neither gas nor electricity – use paraffin. We bought a few things from an antique shop.

Mary and Betty (Mary's sister) came back to England in 1975. They stayed overnight in the Bull hotel in Peterborough. Her diary continues 'Tuesday July 1st 1975 Market Deeping:-
Bets and I left Peterborough about 8.30 a.m. and drove directly to Market Deeping, 8 miles. We spent most of the day here and loving every minute. As a very young man (1899 – 1909) our dad managed the distillery (extraction of essential oils from lavender, mints, wormwood, etc.)After buying a few postcards (we were parked in the village square) Bets got 'caught' trying to unlock some other lady's butterscotch car's trunk (boot)! We must have talked an hour to Mr Stacey, owner of the jewellery store – although he's been here only since 1947, he has in his 30 years become like the village archivist. About 65, bushy browed he was marvellous! If only I'd had Betty's tape recorder – tons I hope to remember. The jeweller directed us to the STILL where Mrs Adams (83) and her brother (Mr Ball) and wife still live in the house adjoining the distillery. We had met Mrs Adams in1962. Betty visited with her while I went with Mr Ball to the very top of the ruins of the still (built in1846). He described a small bay window where our dad would have 'surveyed' the workers in the fields of lavender, etc
I got 3 pieces of slate from the roof area to take home. Over the years people have removed everything from the numerous rooms (laboratory etc.) but Mr Ball, when we exited the still, went into the house, brought back a lovely old blue bottle that would have been in the laboratory and gave it to us – we were ecstatic!!!

From the Still we went to the rectory, the oldest inhabited rectory in England – we met the vicar (rector) and Mrs Davies who took us over the rectory – such utter, utter beauty is not describable here – room after room had been restored, all stark white with black timbers, scarlet carpeting.

Mary Vinton visited again in 1985 – her diary of Saturday 4th May relates:-
Visited Tulip fields in the Fens, traffic awful! In a 20 minute queue I had time to photo canal scene in the Fens. At Market Deeping we left tulip tour and decided to fuss around where our dad had started his career in

essential oils – we'd been there in '62 and '75. We were amazed to find Mrs Adams (the STILL) still alive at 93 – blind but alert - so very pleased to see us – also warmly welcomed by her brother, Mr Ball. Later enjoyed a coffee in the charming architecture of the precinct. Amazed at fields now housing estates – streets named Thyme, Lavender Lane, Spearmint Drive, etc. Never have enough time in Market Deeping.

Mary Vinton visited England again in 1988. During that visit she called on a Mr Brian Kingston who had retired and was researching the essential oils and perfumery business. Mr Kingston had been trying to find information about the Holland essential oil distillery so Mary gave him the blueprints of the laboratory and distillery that her father (Richard F. Stroud) had taken to America. Mary says that Mr Kingston assured her that the plans would be preserved in London. In her letter dated March 1st 1998, Mary says that Brian Kingston had been ill when they visited in 1988 and sadly died some months later.

The extensive notes made by Brian Kingston during his research into the essential oils and perfumery industries were, as he promised, deposited in London, more precisely in the Wellcome Museum for History in Medicine in Euston Road. I have been through the two large boxes of notes and drawings on two separate occasions and, unfortunately, have been unable to locate the plans of the Market Deeping distillery. I have, however, been able to glean some information from Brian Kingston's notes and I would like to acknowledge my gratitude to him for the work he carried out. I mentioned earlier that the information about this business was very sketchy but being able to see this research material enabled me to shed a little more light on this subject.

Mary and her sister visited Market Deeping again in 1991 where they had lunch at the 'Bull'. She says her dad would have known it well. She also paid a visit to the distillery to see Mr Ball. Mary and her sister Betty visited England again in 1994 and 1996. The letters I received from Mary Vinton were very helpful to this project and I am indebted to her for the information that she sent.

'The Notes of Richard F. Stroud'

1836: Holland's Distillery at Market Deeping, Lincolnshire, England, was built.

5 copper stills, 5 pewter worm condensers (average capacity about one ton of herb.)

1899: Tramped my first stillful. Hoisted first charge by hand operated windlass in this distillery.

1905: Replaced old worn out condenser with new Bennett, Sons & Shears. Ideal annular concentric condenser, finest made. Exported English Black Peppermint roots to E.K. Warren, Three Oaks, Michigan, U.S.A.

1909: Migrated to America

Mary Vinton copied out her father's notes on one year's output from Holland's distillery at Market Deeping. These undated jottings give a list of the various extracts produced by the Market Deeping Distillery in one year. I have included, in brackets, the use to which medical practitioners during the last century might have put some of the substances. The information regarding substances produced by the Market Deeping distillery has been shown to a person who has been involved in the essential oil distilling business for many years. He suggests that the information regarding quantities might be in error. Having no other information, I can only list below the notes sent to me by Mrs Vinton.

Extract of Belladonna vivid - 2,000lbs;
Scammony Resin (was used as a purgative) - 1,500lbs;
Extract of Gentian (used to treat impetigo) 800lbs.
Also listed, with no stated quantities were Bismuth Carbonate; Bismuth Subnitrate; Ferri et Quince Citrate; Ammonium Bromide and Magnesium Carbonate Powder.
Also various effervescent preparations – Antipyrine; Caffein Citrate; potassium Citrate; Lithium Citrate; Magnesium Citrate; Sodium Citro-Tartarate and Piperazin.

Two acids were listed, namely Hydrocyanic acid and Hydrofluoric acid, however I feel that it is unlikely that they were actually 'manufactured' at Market Deeping distillery. They may have been bought in bulk (wholesale) to be transferred to smaller containers to be sold as retail products or used in one or other of the processes carried out in the distillery.

For anyone interested to read further there is an article on the internet showing a photograph of a young Richard F. Stroud (just Google the name Richard F Stroud). The article states that Richard F. Stroud was the manager of the A. M. Todd plantation at Mentha, Michigan and that he invented the first portable mint stilling tubs in America. The article goes on to explain that, in America, with the widespread use of portable units, the old stationary round tubs units have become archaic relics and that only a few still remain standing today. Further details of the very extensive A. M. Todd Company as it is today (2008) can also be found on the internet.

Mary Vinton included a typed copy of the letter that was sent by her father, Richard F. Stroud, to the Editor of the Spalding Free Press in 1936. The copy is signed Richard F. Stroud.

Mentha, Michigan, U.S.A.
January 28th 1936

The Editor
Spalding Free Press
Spalding,
Lincs.
England

Dear Sir:

It may be of interest to you or some of your readers that I have in my possession the original plans of a proposed new laboratory for W. Holland Esq. of Market Deeping. They are dated March 28th 1834. Also the plans of a proposed new distillery for the same gentleman dated 24th March 1836. There is little doubt that all the plans were drawn by the same architect as they are dated at Northorpe in the same handwriting but no signature appears on them.

I operated the Market Deeping Distillery from 1899 to 1909 and there received the first insight into a business which is perhaps unique. At one time the late Squire Holland, who died early in 1899 I believe, farmed several hundred acres of land and grew peppermint, lavender, rosemary, dill, wormwood, henbane, belladonna, aconite, foxglove, opium poppies, dandelions and other essential-oil and drug plants. Unfortunately this unique and world wide known business is as dead as the dodo at Market Deeping.

Four thousand miles away in the south-western corner of Michigan there flourishes an enormous industry along these lines. Somewhere between twenty and twenty-five thousand acres of black land very similar to the land in Deeping Fen but called, in America, 'Muck Land' is devoted to essential oil plants, mostly peppermint and spearmint.

Since 1910 I have managed the largest farm in this group and we grow and distil annually over one thousand acres of peppermint and spearmint. In 1925 I designed and built an ultra modern peppermint distilling plant with a capacity of forty acres per day. The capacity of the Market Deeping plant was never more than two acres per day. Machinery has been developed during the past twenty five years that eliminates most of the hand work in planting, cultivating, weeding, harvesting and distilling these crops. After the quiet and leisurely way these crops were handled at Market Deeping one could imagine himself transferred into Dantes Inferno when we are in full swing. A good day's run at Market Deeping might produce sixty pounds (27.3 kilograms) by weight of peppermint oil whereas we have, on several occasions, run out over a ton (1,120 kilograms) of the oil in a day.

During the Second World War this farm grew sufficient henbane to prevent a famine in this drug in America. Formerly its entire supply was received from Europe. In twenty six years in America I have seen mass production, mass prosperity, mass depression, mass bank failures and mass poverty amongst its people.

I have missed most the quiet fishing by the Welland, the keen inter-village football games in which I took part, the fun of the village whist drives, the delights of the town fairs and the skating from Peakirk to Crowland and at Cowbit. In lieu of all these pleasures I have raised in comfort a fine family of three girls and a boy, built up a reasonable estate from nothing, own a couple of motor cars and drive annually eighteen to twenty thousand miles mostly for recreation and visited the old country seven times. Mr. Joe Seymour of Holbeach is the only man I know who still grows peppermint in your neighbourhood. One of my greatest treats is to visit him and his good family when I am in England.

And that's enough from a dam yank.
Yours very sincerely
(Signed) Richard F. Stroud

Here is an article that appeared in a newspaper sometime after 1947. Unfortunately the name of the publication is not included in the cutting I saw. Although this article contained some of the information given in the letter above, I feel it should be included in its entirety because, as it appears to have been written by a reporter who, I assume, interviewed Richard F. Stroud, it gives a fuller picture of what happened to Mr Stroud after he left Market Deeping distillery. It also explains how he implemented a business in America using the experience he gained in this relatively little village in Lincolnshire.

It is important that the reader understands that all the information written in this article should not be taken at face value. For example Richard Stroud refers to 'Squire' William Holland having built the distillery. The person who was referred to as 'Squire' William Holland was, in fact the son of one of the founders, William Holland (surgeon). The distillery building was constructed sometime shortly after the plans were drawn up (late 1830s/early 1840s). Young (Squire) William Holland took over the running of the distillery some time around 1850 by which time the business had been already running successfully for approximately 10 years. The confusion arises, I feel, because both men were named William Holland.

Story of an American Project

From time to time much has been written about the former peppermint dis-tillery which flourished in the latter part of last century and the early part of this at Market Deeping. Now we publish a story of a thriving American business, to the success of which its pioneer, Mr. Richard F. Stroud, attributes all he learned at the Market Deeping distillery. The Deeping distillery built in Tinker's lane (*now called Godsey Lane*) by the late Squire William Holland flourished in the latter half of the last century and the early part of this until the First World War. It provided much both at Market Deeping at the factory and in the fields where crops for the distillery were grown.

Mr. Stroud writes from 511 Grand Pie-Avenue, Kalamazoo. Michigan.
'While cleaning up my workshop in the basement I ran across some drawings which may interest someone in the vicinity of Market Deeping. The drawings were made at Northorpe on 1st March 24th 1836 for

W. Holland Esq. of Market Deeping for a new distillery and laboratory to be built there (according to a letter Richard wrote to the Spalding Free Press in 1936, the laboratory plans were dated 1834 and those for the distillery 1836).

Ten years grounding
During the period 1899 to 1909 I obtained my grounding in the mysteries of the production of essential oils and pharmaceutical products at this very plant. Then I migrated to America and first became assistant superintendent and finally superintendent of the properties of the A. M. Todd Company's 2,140 acres of peat land at Mentha, Michigan. All but 500 acres of this land was then covered with timber and bush. A small distillery, a sawmill, a huge barn, a blacksmith's shop, warehouse, company store, a few houses and some 40 work horses comprised the whole community. Labour was mostly transient known in America as 'hobos' and in England as 'tramps'.

Cleared land
Over the years we cleared land, sawed up the timber, built other houses. We produced crops of peppermint, spearmint, wormwood, dill onions, sugar beet, rutabagas (rutabagas are vegetables very similar to turnips except that they generally have yellowish flesh) celery, cabbage and carrots, all of which were shipped by car loads to cities in Michigan and Illinois and some to New York. A branch line of the Michigan Central Rail Road ran through Mentha and a siding was provided.

In 1942 I drew the plans for a huge distillery capable of distilling 40 acres of mint per day all to be handled mechanically under a new idea which originated in my small skull. These plans were O K'd by the Todd Company and I superintended the building which proved highly successful. As much as 1,000 acres (414.7 hectares) were distilled in a single season.

Entirely new
During the wars years 1914 – 1918 and 1939 – 1945 I also grew large acreages of belladonna, henbane, strammarium (*strammarium is the word printed in the original article but I can find no reference to this substance and wonder if it is a reporting error and meant to be stramonium*), digitalis, etc., and erected a drying plant with a tray area of more than one acre (0.41 hectares), heated by steam coils. This business was entirely new to America

so we were able to prevent a famine in these drugs which were previously imported from Europe. The financial results were phenomenal as you can possibly guess. To all of the above I owe my experiences gained in Market Deeping at the old distillery and laboratory of which I have the original plans.

Mr. Stroud says since he emigrated he has re-visited England several times, on one of these trips he married a Rugby girl, they have three daughters and of a son. Two daughters are married and the other daughter and son, who live at home, are school teachers. Mr. Stroud has been living at Kalamazoo since his retirement in 1947.

Old Friends
To all my friends in Market Deeping who still remember me I say Hello, especially to Jim Thorpe (of the Mill) and Fred Otter - both good sports.
Mr. Stroud adds that of the bunch of men he took over to America from the Spalding district the best one was Richard Caley of Long Sutton. Of Mr. Caley he writes: He now lives in a suburb of Kalamazoo and has a wife and four grownup sons, owns two houses, has worked for the Michigan State Highway Commission for the past 20 years and is due to retire next year on a pension and will also get social security payments.

CHAPTER EIGHT

Other Essential Oil Distilleries.

When the Market Deeping essential oil distillery was put up for sale in 1899, the Auctioneer remarked that some of the largest and best country seats were, at that time, occupied by gentlemen who had made their 'pile' in the business of essential oil distillation. It will therefore come as no surprise to learn that Market Deeping was not alone in the business. Not only were there many other essential oil distilleries, there were others in the vicinity of Market Deeping.

There was an essential oil distillery at Peterborough which, I believe, was founded by Mr Scrimshire who was the apothecary (pharmacist) at the local Infirmary. The infirmary building, in Priestgate, now houses Peterborough Museum and Art Gallery. The distillery itself was located at Holywell in Longthorpe, a small village on the outskirts of the town. The main products of this distillery were lavender and peppermint. Later the distillery was run by his son, the Rev. Scrimshire of Longthorpe. Unfortunately the Rev. Scrimshire found that he was unable to manage the day to day running of an essential oil distillery whilst maintaining his duties as a parish priest. He asked William Holland of the Market Deeping distillery, to manage it for him. The actual ownership of the distillery was kept by the Rev. Scrimshire.

There was said to be a distillery at Crowland (about 7 miles from Market Deeping). The information I have regarding this distillery comes from an article in the 'Peterborough Advertiser' dated August 22nd 1908. The author of the article places the actual distillery between Thorney and Crowland. He or she remarks upon the smell that pervaded the atmosphere describing it as associated with a pharmacy or a soothing cordial rather than the open countryside. The farm, Abbey farm, was owned by Mr. Perkins Bellairs. He grew 16 acres of peppermint which was harvested with a 'grass mower', left for two days to shrink a little in order to allow easier transporting. It was then packed into the coppers for processing.

There were three coppers in the distillery, each of which held about 5cwt. (approximately 227 kilograms) of herb at a time. At the bottom of each copper was about two feet of water, and over this was a false floor on which rested the mint. When the copper had been filled, the lid was fitted into a water-joint to prevent steam from escaping (suggesting that steam extraction was used for processing). From the apex of each lid projected a pipe which was connected with a tube running round and round a large condenser filled with cold water. As the steam from the copper ran through this tube it again became liquid and finally dripped out into a vessel shaped something like an enormous coffee pot. The construction of this 'coffee pot' was apparently a trade secret. The idea of it was to enable the oil to become separated from the water, which would run off and leave the precious essence behind. This water, called peppermint water, was allowed to run to waste unless begged by the neighbours. With the addition of a little sugar it was said to make an agreeable drink. Five hours is considered to be the proper time to keep the mint in the copper in order to obtain all its essence.

Mr. Bellairs expressed the opinion at that time there would never be a revival of peppermint cultivation in the fen district. "The soil is certainly suitable", he said, "but the large initial outlay and the keen foreign competition will deter people from putting their capital into it. My still, with full equipment, cost £1,000 and the expenses of upkeep are very heavy. It was built by my father forty years ago, and has been in constant use ever since". "The bulk of foreign peppermint comes from Japan" He said, "Japanese oil of peppermint can be bought at 4/6d (22.5p) a pound, whereas we cannot produce it for less that about 24/-(£1.20p). It is a striking proof of the immense superiority of the English variety that we can find any market at all" he declared. He went on to explain that he thought the reason why the Japanese can under-sell producers like him, to such an extent, is because of the cheapness of labour out there. He said that "Labour is a very large item in peppermint growing. For the sixteen acres that I have at present under cultivation, I employ 10 men for a fortnight in the spring, 12 women all the summer to keep it free from weeds and six men for three weeks in the busy month of August to do distilling. An average crop is worth from £20 to £25 gross per acre. I have known it to fetch anything from £40 to £45, but £25 is a fair average, and shows a satisfactory margin of profit".

There resided in Newborough, at Norwood House, near Peterborough a peppermint distillery under the apparent ownership of J. and A. H. Bellairs. The evidence of the existence of such a business is through a label and an invoice I have seen. Perkins Bellairs Crowland distillery was described in the above article as being between Crowland and Thorney. Newborough, although not on a direct line between Crowland and Thorney could be described as being situated between those two places and therefore this might be the same distillery mentioned in the 'Crowland' article. The name of the business on the label is J. & A. H. Bellairs, Distillers, Newborough, Peterboro'. On the invoice the name is given as William Bellairs, Peppermint Grower and Distiller. The invoice is dated 14th March 1899. I have included pictures of the invoice and both sides of the label.

There was also an essential oil distillery at Holbeach in Lincolnshire and here again peppermint was the main product. It was located in what is now called Distillery Farm. Not only do I have details of the products, I also have some photographs taken inside the building. The following is a transcript of a poor quality photo-copy which purports to be from the 'Peterborough Chronicle' of 1923, although the reference to the 'Spalding Guardian' suggests that the article may have been published in that journal.

A New South Lincolnshire Industry

Just outside Holbeach there is a peppermint distillery, employing four men, and as the industry of peppermint distillation is so little known in England, a representative of the 'Spalding Guardian' paid a visit to Mr. Joseph Seymour's little factory out of pure curiosity. Travellers along the Spalding to Holbeach Road will have been attracted by the pungent aroma of the twelve acres of peppermint which lies to the right of it. The scent pervades the air to even a greater extent now that the crop is being cut, dried, and carted to the distillery. Following the track of one of these carts the writer at last came upon Mr. Seymour in the still room where he was stoking to the accompaniment of a running tap and the faint hiss of steam.

"This is a new industry of yours, isn't it, Mr. Seymour?"

"Oh no, I have been in it all my life. I am a Whaplode man, and before I came to Holbeach three years ago, I used to distil the peppermint there".

"Is it a profitable undertaking?"

"I'll tell you I would rather have twelve acres under a good crop of potatoes this year," forcibly replied Mr. Seymour. "We have to compete against the foreigners, and there is a lot of expense attached to the trade. The Japanese and Americans have the bulk of the peppermint trade."

Our representative was given to understand, however, that potatoes were not preferable to peppermint every year. Mr. Seymour further explained that about three tons of peppermint herbs were dried, cleansed, and distilled every day. These processes demanded a good supply of water and a well fourteen feet across the bottom was kept almost dry by the constantly working pumps.

Holbeach distillery

The distillation is converted into a refreshing and heat-producing winter cordial for cyclists and motorists, in which a healthy wholesale trade is done throughout the country.

Naturally, there is no demand for the liquid, which is absolutely non-alcoholic, in summer. This means that in the busiest season, when the capital has to be expended on labour, the trade is absolutely at a standstill. Mr. Seymour declared that he had no intention of increasing the acreage of his peppermint fields. Having accepted an invitation to drink a glass of the cordial, which while refreshing, was certainly a little too hot for an August day, the writer wished Mr. Seymour good day.

I was contacted by Paul Beard who had information about the Holbeach distillery and I am very grateful to him for giving me permission to make use of the following notes that he made. I am also grateful that he was able to obtain photographs of the inside of the building that showed the two large boilers and associated condensers. Paul produced his notes on 'Essential Oil Distilleries in the Holbeach Area' in January, 1997. I reproduce a transcript below:

Mr. Colin Seymour of Holbeach whose family owned the only known distillery in the Holbeach area, provided most of the information in this paper.

Mr. Colin Seymour's grandfather (Joseph) first became interested in distillation while he was in America. It is believed that he may previously have been involved in the Klondike Gold Rush. Whatever, he subsequently lived in Kalamazoo, Michigan, where he learnt the distillation process. (*Coincidentally Richard F. Stroud, who worked at the Market Deeping distillery from 1899 until he emigrated to America in 1909, lived in Michigan and worked at A. M. Todd's peppermint distillery in the town of Mentha. He remarked in an article in the Spalding Free Press in 1936, 'that Mr. Joe Seymour of Holbeach is the only man I know who still grows peppermint in your neighbourhood'*).

He returned to England and in about 1923 set up his first still at what became known as 'Peppermint Farm' in Whaplode. This was probably a fairly cobbled together affair. However, it was clearly successful since he installed a professionally built still at what became 'Distillery Farm' next to what is now the A17 at Holbeach. This was in about 1926. The business passed

101

A 'can' used in the Holbeach distillery
to separate the
essential oil from the water

subsequently to Mr. Colin Seymour's father (Joseph William) and later to Mr. Colin Seymour.

Mr. Alan Seymour (Mr. Colin Seymour's brother) has photographs and hopes to provide copies. (*Paul later sent me copies of the photographs one of which is included in this book*).

The main product was peppermint oil, although coriander and dill were also distilled there. Other plants including lavender and poppies were known to be treated by similar processes elsewhere. The peppermint plant which turned purple when it ripened (similar to the peppermint found in domestic gardens today) was grown for three or sometimes four years before being ploughed in. It was not grown from seed but suckers were taken from near the roots of the plants in May of the second year and planted into new areas to start a new 3/4 year cycle.

The biggest problem was weeding. Suitable sprays were not then available and the job was very labour-intensive and therefore very expensive. The first year was not too difficult as the plants were in straight rows allowing horse-drawn or mechanical hoes to be used. In subsequent years as the plants meandered around, only hand weeding was possible.

In winter the peppermint fields were ploughed to a depth of 3 or 4 inches (approximately 10 cms). Very accurate ploughing was required if the plants were not to be disturbed. The crop was harvested with hay-cutting machinery and left in the field for two days to wilt and lose some 50% of its water content. The crop had a pungent peppermint smell which pervaded the clothes of those working with it. Local bee keepers approved of the crop which enabled their bees to produce a superior honey. It was important to cut and process the crop at the right time. A colourless oil was required and even a delay of three days could result in a darker product.

The peppermint crop would be distilled during a two week period in mid August. An acre (0.41 hectares) of peppermint filled the copper three times, each producing some 5 lbs (approximately 2.3 kilograms) of oil. i.e. 15 lbs (approximately 6.8 kilograms) per acre. The distillation took only a short time but only three copper-loads could be treated per day because of the work involved in loading and emptying the copper. Emptying the copper was particularly hard work and the 'used' plants were later ploughed into the land. This was not considered particularly beneficial to the land but simply the best way to dispose of the waste material. The distilled oil and water was poured into copper cans, not unlike large watering cans, and allowed to separate. After the water/oil mixture had separated the oil, which had floated to the top, was poured off through the spout. The oil was then stored in glass carboys which held about 1.5 gallons (approximately 6.8 litres) which weighed approximately 5lbs (2.3 kilograms).

Mr. Colin Seymour considers that no great technical knowledge was required such that a 'recipe' would need to have been written down, however he is aware that older distillers such as his father and grandfather encouraged a mystique about the process, no doubt to discourage

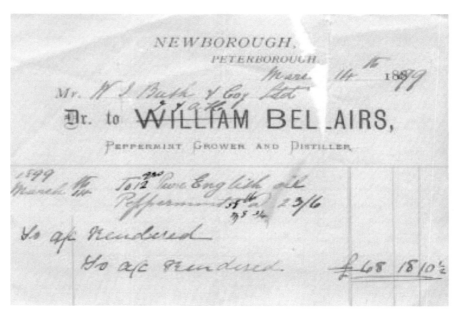

NEWBOROUGH,
PETERBOROUGH.

March 14th 1899

Mr. *W J Bath & Coy Ltd*

Dr. to **WILLIAM BELLAIRS,**

PEPPERMINT GROWER AND DISTILLER

1899
March 14   To 12 Pure English oil
Peppermint 55th   23/6
95 1/4

To a/c Rendered

To a/c Rendered.   £68 18 10½

An invoice dated March 14th 1899
from Bellairs distillery

GLASS WITH CARE.   This side up.

From   **J. & A. H. BELLAIRS**
DISTILLERS.

PLEASE REVERSE THIS CARD.

Newborough, Peterborough.

Label of the type used by Bellairs distillery

104

competition. Coriander and Dill were grown for the still by four or five local farmers. This was not as profitable as peppermint but since it was the seed which was processed, it could be distilled at a convenient time during the winter.

Samples of the oil would be sent to purchasers (mainly to wholesalers Messrs. Hobbs of Tower Hill and also to the British Drug House and a sweet manufacturer). An offer would be made (about £20 per lb. {£44 per kilogram} during the 1950s) and in due course the year's product would be delivered to London in a Land Rover.

The process eventually became unprofitable due to the high labour costs and competition from a cheap (although inferior) product from Brazil. The Holbeach still ceased to work in about 1958. Mr. Seymour is certain that there were no other essential oil stills working in the Holbeach area at this time and had not heard of one in Market Deeping. He does however recall one existing in Long Melford, Suffolk.

The following article entitled 'A Peppermint Distillery at Holbeach', by Mrs. C. M. Wilson, appeared in the Journal of Lincolnshire Industrial Archaeology. Volume 8 Number 1 (1973)

It is surprising how often the name of a farm, house or street can give a clue to interesting activities which once took place there, if only one has time to follow them up. Distillery Farm, Holbeach, is a good example. Although of comparatively recent origin, the distilling which took place there was obviously sufficiently unusual in the area to give its name to the farm.

During a recent visit to Distillery Farm, the owner, Mr. Colin Seymour, was good enough to supply details about the growing and distilling of peppermint on his farm. The equipment consisted of a boiler and two vats or coppers about 10 ft. (3.1 metres) high and 6 ft. (1.85 metres) in diameter, very similar in appearance to those used in whisky distilleries. These were installed by Mr. Seymour's grandfather about 1926 but there is no clue as to where they were made.

The farm grew 10-12 acres (4.1 – 4.8 hectares) of peppermint each year, the crop being cut like hay and then transported to the barn containing the distilling equipment. The coppers were filled with peppermint and the lid secured in position. Steam was then passed through the copper, taking with it the peppermint oil and this was condensed into a mixture of oil and water. The oil was separated out in a separator and bottled for dispatch to the manufacturers of confectionery. Each copper-full produced 5 lbs. (2.3 kilograms) of oil and a copper could be filled three times from an acre of the crop. Thus 10 acres (4.1 hectares) would produce some 150 lbs. (69 kilograms) of peppermint oil.

It was, Mr. Seymour said, quite a worthwhile crop particularly during and just after the last war. The actual distilling process took about one and a half hours but filling and emptying the coppers was quite time consuming so that only three copper loads could be distilled in a day. The main reason for discontinuing the growing of peppermint at Distillery Farm was that it was not possible to mechanise the process any further and high labour costs made it uneconomical. Also there was heavy competition from imported peppermint which now supplies most of the demand. To make more use of the equipment the farm also grew and distilled coriander and dill, the essence being used in the manufacture of gripe water, etc. The equipment is still in situ though it has not been used for 15 years.

The above is a very superficial look at an unusual but interesting aspect of Lincolnshire's agricultural/industrial past and one hopes that someone sometime will have the opportunity to study the subject in more depth, though the equipment at Holbeach is likely to be scrapped within the year. Mr. Seymour knew of no other peppermint distillery in the Holbeach area and I know of no others in the Fens. If any member knows of other places where peppermint was grown and/or distilled, I should be very interested to hear about it.

Postscript

The story of the Holland's essential oil distillery did not end when August Paven was declared bankrupt in 1921. The buildings themselves may no longer have been used for their original purpose but the name 'Holland's Essential Oils' lived on. The following information is partly based on the notes of Brian Kingston that are held in the Wellcome Museum for History in Medicine, Euston Road, London: -

'Holland's Distillery', established in 1840, incorporating 'Messrs J. & G. Miller' of Mitcham, Surrey. The firm of J. and G. Miller began life in 1865. Millers originally distilled their own plant material as well as contracting work for other growers. There were three sons who all lived at Mill Green Road. After incorporation the firm became Holland's Distillery (Essential Oils) Ltd in 1913; the business expanded the contract distilling business from plants supplied by growers mainly within an eight mile radius of Mitcham. They mainly processed peppermint, lavender and camomile.

Brian Kingston's notes give some detail about the original 'J & G Miller' distillery in Mitcham in Surrey that incorporated Holland's distillery, but an article in the Perfumery & Essential Oil Record (annual special number) dated 1933, explains more fully what happened to the Holland name after 1913.

HOLLAND'S DISTILLERY LTD. (ESSENTIAL OILS) LIMITED.
ESTABLISHED MARKET DEEPING 1840.
Terpeneless Oil Specialists.
37 & 39, WOOD ST.,
MITCHAM,
SURREY.

HOLLAND'S DISTILLERY (ESSENTIAL OILS) LTD. was established at Market Deeping, in Lincolnshire, in the year 1840 by William Holland. Herbs were

Perfumers ——

WHEN substituting TERPENELESS or SESQUITERPENELESS oils in place of natural oils, make positively sure of the degree of CONCENTRATION. Price is not a criterion. We manufacture nothing but the finest qualities with the highest standard of purity.

HOLLANDS STANDARD TERPENELESS

Foreign-made products are incomparable.

Use the Finest Terpeneless Oils and make sure by buying from

HOLLANDS DISTILLERY LTD.

(ESSENTIAL OILS) LIMITED.

ESTABLISHED MARKET DEEPING 1840.

Terpeneless Oil Specialists

37 & 39, WOOD ST., MITCHAM, SURREY.

grown there and distilled, and medicinal products were also produced. The present company was incorporated in 1913 with a capital of £10,000. In the following year they entered into the manufacture of terpeneless oils, being the first British house to undertake this production. They have one of the finest plants for this manufacture and produce terpeneless and sesquiterpeneless oils of the highest possible standard. The distillery is situated in rather rural surroundings; orchards and glass-houses giving a pleasant outlook.

A tributary of the River Wandle passes through the property, and the soft water from this is used by the firm for condensing purposes and boilers. The vacuum pumps used are of the latest type, capable of creating to within one-fifth of a millimetre of absolute vacuum. This high vacuum permits working under very low boiling temperature, with the result that the manufacture of terpeneless oils produces the finished product without the slightest trace of burning, besides allowing the extraction of terpenes at their low temperature evaporation point. 'Holland's Standard Terpeneless' represents the degree of concentration and solubility recognised by the trade as standard quality.

The firm has recently built new offices on their Mitcham freehold, deciding that it is in the interests of their clients to be in closer contact with the manufacturing side of the business. They have just occupied this new accommodation, vacating their old administrative premises at 26, Denman Street, London, S.E. The company has the sole European handling of Ezra K. Hollington's Peppermint, an oil produced from Mitcham plants and grown and distilled in the United States. They are also distillers of Mitcham peppermint, distilling the herb every autumn for farmers growing in the surrounding districts.

I made enquiries in the Mitcham area and could find no information about this company either under its original name or the one it acquired after 1913. Knowing that J & G Miller/Holland's Distillery (Essential Oils) Ltd. was a registered company I contacted Company's House and received the following reply:-

HOLLAND'S DISTILLERY (ESSENTIAL OILS) LTD.

Thank you for your recent enquiry concerning the above company name. I have searched our records and found the following information:-
Company Number: 126302.
Incorporation Date: Around 1912.
Company Status: Dissolved - 15/09/1983.

As you can see, the name of one of the founders lived on in a town in Surrey for many years after the original business, in Market Deeping, ceased trading. The original building, where all the essential oils and medicines were manufactured, survived until late in 2006 when it was replaced by a small group of houses. The buildings where the many processes were carried out may have disappeared but the memory of the 'Market Deeping Essential Oil Distillery and Medicinal Manufacture' remains. Bramley, Rosemary, Thyme and Clover have been used for the names of avenues and roads in the immediate area. Part of the roadway that led from Holland House to the distillery now contains a small group

of houses and is aptly named 'Still Close'. It is unfortunate that so much has been lost of the detail of what actually took place in the distillery during the time it was in production but, maybe one day, someone will erect a sign marking the place where this world famous essential oils distillery once stood.